Principles Of Conformation Analysis

Volume II

By Deb Bennett, PhD

Executive Editor: Bobbie Lieberman
Medical Editor: Matthew Mackay-Smith, DVM
Contributing Editors: Mary Beth de Ribeaux,
    Leslie Jo Kelley, Mary Kay Kinnish
Art Director: Kathy Egbert

President: Ami Shinitzky
Publisher: Susan Harding

ISBN: 1-929164-06-8

D1067209

*For Sadie, my friend
and patient teacher*

Contents

Chapter 1: How To Look At A Horse's Back
Examining the seat of equine performance   5
Exercise 1: A Look At The Loin
Exercise 2: The Telltale Topline
Exercise 3: Evaluating The "Transmission"
Exercise 4: Of Mutton And The Mighty Camel
Exercise 5: Ropes And Ladders
Exercise 6: When The Ring Of Muscles Breaks Down

Chapter 2: How To Look At A Horse's Neck
Of length, balance and the paradox of flexibility . .   35
Exercise 1: A Menagerie Of Necks
Exercise 2: The Long And Short Of Equine Necks
Exercise 3: Getting To The Root Of Ewe Neck
Exercise 4: The Ideal Equine Neck

Chapter 3: How To Look At A Horse's Forequarter
Standing or in motion, it's what's up front that
counts   59
Exercise 1: The Right Angle On Shoulders
Exercise 2: The Lesser-Known Arm Bone
Exercise 3: Foundation Of The Forelimbs
Exercise 4: When Arms Are Assymetrical
Exercise 5: See How They Stand
Exercise 6: Putting The Knee In Perspective
Exercise 7: The Links Of The Forelimb

Epilogue: The Gift Of Lightness
How an uncooperative riding horse was
transformed into a graceful, athletic mount   92

Appendix A:
Deep and shallow muscles of the horse's back and
neck   95

Appendix B:
Shoulder and breast muscles of the horse   96

Figure 1. When palpating a horse's back, use the pads of your fingers, and cover the whole expanse from withers to loins. In these two photos, I am pressing firmly to demonstrate the effect of an ill-fitting saddle; when palpating to find "knots" and cold spots, you do not need to dent the flesh. In photo A, gouging the withers near or under the fore arch elicits fasciculation (vibrating waves of muscle contraction), even from this otherwise normal back. In B, gouging the loins elicits the same involuntary but debilitating reaction.

Chapter 1

How To Look At A Horse's Back

Examining the seat of equine performance

This volume of *Principles Of Conformation Analysis* continues the theme established in the first volume of this series — the functional importance of the horse's back. While the horse's forelimbs are the structural equivalent of the wheels and suspension system in an automobile, and his hindquarters are equivalent to the motor and drive train, his back acts as the transmission — the part which connects the motor to the wheels and which serves to regulate the amount of power that flows through.

Nobody wants to drive a car that has flat tires, bent rims or a sagging suspension, although in an emergency it is possible to do so. Likewise, a car without a motor isn't going to go far — unless you push it over the top of a hill, whereupon it will travel as far as gravity allows. However, a car without a transmission is truly nonfunctional: revving the motor or turning the steering wheel will get you exactly nowhere. In a similar way, it's important to realize that not all the weaknesses and lamenesses which afflict the ridden horse are native to the legs — the back is quite often literally and figuratively the "seat" of the problem.

A Feel For Tonus

Even before you begin to look at a horse's back, you should learn how to feel (palpate) it. There's no other way to determine the *tonus* — the natural muscle tone — of a given back. Physiologically speaking, tonus is the slight continuous contraction which is present at all times in live muscle tissue. You can feel the tonus present in your arm muscles right now simply by pressing your left forearm with your right index finger. See how the muscle tissue springs back to shape when you remove your finger? That's due to tonus. If you're seated and relaxed as you read this paragraph, it won't take very much force to dent your arm muscles. The slight contraction in your arm muscles, which results in a slight springiness, is called resting tonus. If you are sound asleep when tested for tonus, the dent in your arm would still spring back, but not quite as quickly as when you are awake. Tonus falls still further in a comatose person. A dead body has no tonus; pressure makes a dent, but the dent doesn't spring back.

At the other end of the spectrum lie excited and fearful states. Tense the muscles of your left forearm, and again try to dent them. Now it's much harder to make a dent, and when you remove your pressing finger, the muscles spring back to shape almost instantly.

You've just examined the wide range of tonus which your own body can produce. However, there are also variations in resting tonus, which is the starting or "zero point" of this range. These variations show up in comparing one person, or one horse, to another. Most important for judging excellence and suitability in a horse, increases in resting tonus tend to accompany increases in muscular *reactivity* — the ability of a given muscle to fire the instant it receives electrochemical stimulation. Just as some people have exceptionally fast reflexes, some horses have muscles which are able to react to stimulation exceptionally fast. Almost without exception, horses which have a high resting tonus show fast reflexes. Breeds which typically exhibit high resting tonus include the Arabian, Akhal-Teke, Thoroughbred and bloodlines of American Quarter Horses especially bred for sprint racing and cutting.

At the other end of the spectrum, the draft and

warmblood breeds usually show low resting tonus. The "buttery" back of the warmblood suits it for dressage, while the same series of exercises can be most difficult to execute on an Arabian. On the other hand, trying to turn back a steer with an American Saddlebred or a European warmblood is usually a losing proposition. In short, resting tonus and the accompanying reactivity form the physiological "background" for the suitability of each breed and individual for a given sport or activity.

With practice, you can obtain a good idea of tonus and reactivity simply by feeling your horse's back. What does tonus in the horse feel like? Tie or have someone hold your horse in a safe, quiet place. If you wish, go through your usual grooming routine. After you've finished brushing the horse, set your tools aside. Pat your horse on the shoulder and then slide your hand, palm down, up onto his back. Palpation is done with the pads of the fingers and thumb by sliding them along the skin with the same motion and the same amount of pressure that it would take to rub a glob of peanut butter off a countertop. This amount of pressure will dent the skin and muscles of the back without poking or gouging them (Figure 1).

Go over the entire back, from directly under the withers in front of where your saddle sits, all the way back to where the loins join the croup. Most horses' backs are fairly wide: feel from the widest point of the ribs of the left side, to the widest point of the ribs on the right side. By practicing back palpation this way, you'll accomplish several things at once:

1) You can compare the "quality" or "feel" of normal resting tonus from one individual to another. With practice, you will get an accurate idea of the characteristic tonus of different breeds.

2) You will become intimate with the bony and muscular anatomy of the horse's back. As a guide, refer to the anatomical drawings in Appendix A.

3) You'll be able to locate bony and muscular abnormalities and asymmetries.

Is This a Good Back?

The precise nature of abnormalities of the horse's back is best determined by a qualified veterinarian. However, from palpation you can develop a general idea of what may be wrong.

7

Abnormalities in the horse's back are revealed by the same standard signs seen in all other body zones — swelling, heat, pain and abnormal tonus. Swelling can be seen and felt; heat (or "cold spots") and zones of excessively high tonus ("knots") can also be felt. Pain is manifested by your horse's reactions to varying pressure — during palpation, saddling or even grooming. Such reactions range from pinned ears, rolling eyes, head tossing and attempts to bite or kick to the classic so-called "cold-backed" reaction in which the horse sinks down, even falls to his knees, in an attempt to avoid pressure on his back. A "cold-backed" horse may be impossible to saddle unless the tack is put on in a set order, and he may need to be longed in order to "get the kinks out" before being mounted. Such signs signify much more than "quirky behavior" — they are the horse's way of telling you that something in the saddle area is (or has been) causing him discomfort or pain.

Visual Inspection

Now that you've gotten close enough to the horse to give his back a thorough examination by feel, it's time to step back to take a look at his conformation. Based on the proportions you discover in this analytical look, you'll decide whether the horse's back is conformed correctly for the sport or activity you have in mind. Keep in mind, however, that a horse with a problem-free back still may not be suitable for you.

Look at a horse's back from three perspectives: the left side, the right side and the top. Viewing the horse from the top is essential, and can be done either by standing on a chair placed out of kicking range behind the horse or by standing on the hood of your car

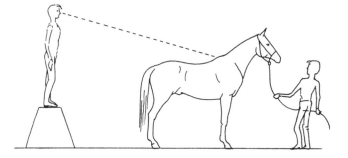

Figure 2. How to visually inspect a horse's back from above.

or a fence (Figure 2).

The most important feature to look for in top view is left-to-right symmetry. In order to accurately assess symmetry, the horse must stand absolutely squarely, with an equal amount of weight on all four feet. Once the horse's feet are "square," ask the handler to gently position the horse's nose exactly in front of the center of his chest.

From your elevated perspective, you should see a ruler-straight topline, all the way from the poll to the dock. In addition, the muscle masses of the left side of the horse should be equal to those of the right side. If they aren't, or if the horse's nose needs to be off to the left or right in order for him to look straight from the top, the horse is asymmetrical in build (Figure 3).

The severity of asymmetry varies. In making this judgment, remember that a slight amount of left-to-right asymmetry is normal for all animals, and people too. For example, the left side of your face is not a mirror image of the right side. Thus, in some horses, part of the mane falls to the left while the rest of it falls to the right. This is indeed a sign of asymmetry, but in most cases the degree of asymmetry which causes it is slight and has little or no effect on the horse's performance.

What you are looking for in this examination are obvious kinks, offsets or twists in the bony or muscular components of the topline. If you're pretty sure that that is what you're seeing in top view, refer to the front-limb section of this volume for further methods of detecting asymmetries.

The movement of the horse also helps to confirm a diagnosis of asymmetrical build. When led in hand, the horse with grossly asymmetrical build cannot move straight forward and will constantly drift, crablike, to one side. In more subtle cases, the horse may consistently refuse to take one lead when longed in a circle. Under saddle, the asymmetrical horse feels as if he has a big hole on one side of him; he's always trying to bump or shift his rider into this hole. Canter departures and turns toward the side with the hole are easy; to the other side, they are much more difficult or impossible.

Severe asymmetries of this kind are congenital or developmental and may primarily affect either the vertebral column or any of the bones which make up the limbs. In most instances, such an individual

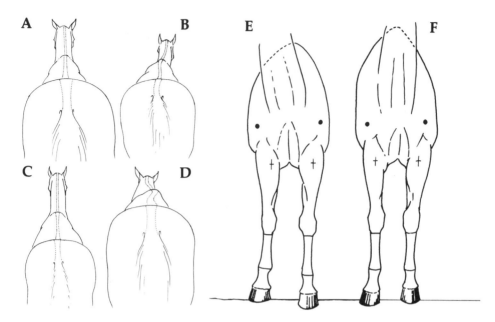

Figure 3. Visual inspection of the horse's back from above may reveal abnormalities. A, most horses look like this — when their feet are "squared up " below and the nose is positioned in front of the breast, the topline from poll to dock is ruler-straight. B, this 12-year-old Anglo-Arabian gelding's topline cannot be made straight even when his feet are square. Physical examination revealed that his right foreleg is about one inch shorter than his left. C, this is how the same gelding looked after physical therapy (a program of being stepped sideways over ground poles) and corrective shoeing by farrier Anthony Gonzales. D, an 8-year-old Arabian gelding with primary scoliosis (curvature of the spine). Despite his spinal deformity, he became a champion hunter-hack, though difficult to ride. His legs are all the same length. E, front view of 12-year-old Anglo-Arabian gelding before therapy and corrective shoeing. F, same horse after correction.

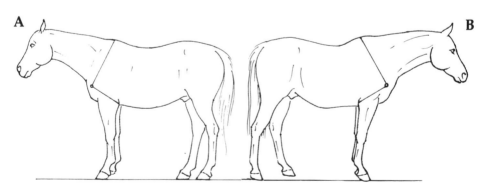

Figure 4. Left and right views of 12-year-old Anglo-Arabian gelding before correction. The gelding's right front leg is one inch shorter than his left. A, "normal" side of horse; the angle formed at the point of shoulder is 93 degrees. B, "short" side of horse; the angle at the point of shoulder is 88 degrees, indicating that this horse compensated for his deformity by compressing his right forelimb, which is evident in front view (Figures 3E, 3F). One of the goals of physical therapy was to stretch the muscles of his right arm and open the shoulder angle on this side.

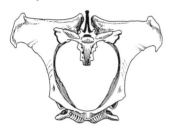

Figure 5. Front and side views of the bony anatomy of the horse's lumbosacral (LS) joint. Top, horse's head toward the viewer; bottom, horse's head to the right.

should be eliminated from further consideration for purchase or breeding.

In Side View

If careful scrutiny of the horse's topline reveals — as it does in most cases — no abnormalities, you can step down from your elevated vantage point and walk around to the right side of the horse. From this angle, you're looking for four main features: the shape and condition of the loins, the shape and condition of the withers, the length of the back in relation to the length of the whole horse, and the internal proportions of the back. When you repeat this procedure from the left side, make one final ground-level check for symmetry (Figure 4). In the exercises that follow, you'll begin learning to judge conformation by example, as you examine the horse's back both from the top and from the sides.

The Back: Lab Exercise 1

A Look At
The Loin

Its structure determines how well a horse can move

In "What Kind Of An Animal Is A Horse?" (Chapter 1 of Volume I), I discussed the evolutionary and functional importance of the loin area or "coupling" in horses. Figure 5 shows the horse's lumbosacral joint (LS), which is the bone structure that actually forms the coupling. This joint is *the* most important one in the horse's body for determining the ability to move well. That's why this book begins with the loin, instead of dealing with the horse's head or front legs.

Analysis

Horse #1: This mare's loin is short and strong; the topline over the lumbosacral joint is smooth; the joint itself is well placed. An ideally placed lumbosacral joint lies as far forward as is anatomically possible — on a line connecting the left and right points of hip. This makes the croup bone (the sacrum) as long as possible which confers a great lever advantage to the horse when he is asked to shorten his underline and flex the LS joint during any movement or exercise requiring collection. At the same time, placing the LS joint far forward shortens the lumbar span of the back. This is good because while the lumbar span is necessary for coiling the loins during collection, it is also the weakest part of the horse's back. Only a minimum length of loin is necessary for loin coiling.

The view from above confirms our observations from the side. A short loin forms a broad triangle. From the side, a strong loin shows no peak or undulation in the topline overlying the LS joint. The upper profile of the back in this area is arched slightly upward.

Horse #2: This mare's loin is long and her back is long, too. The placement of her lumbosacral joint is poor, thus shortening her croup and lengthening a back that would have been long anyway. The longer a horse's back, the weaker and more likely to sag un-

(1) 17-year-old Hungarian-Thoroughbred mare
(2) 24-year-old grade mare
(3) 19-year-old Arab-Quarter Horse mare
(4) 14-year-old Appaloosa gelding

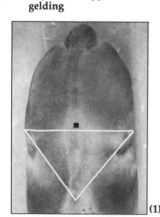

(1)

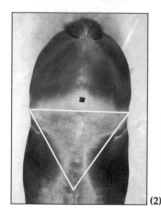

(2)

Courtesy the author

der a rider's weight it tends to be. As a result of her conformation, this mare gives a smooth ride and is good at turns and lateral movements that require her to bend her long rib cage. Movements and exercises that require collection are, however, very difficult for her. In top view, her triangle is longer than it is wide, and her LS joint is located far behind the line connecting her left and right points of hip.

Horse #3: At first glance, in side view this mare's loin appears to be very short. In top view, it is certainly broad. From the side, she visually conforms to an old rule of thumb in conformation judging — that the horse be divisible into three approximately equal masses (neck and shoulder, back and belly, and quarters). However, because her lumbosacral joint is located behind the line connecting the left and right points of hip, this mare's lumbar span is actually as long as Horse #1's (in top view, the lumbar span is measured from the apex of the triangle to the black dot). Because of the rearward placement of her LS

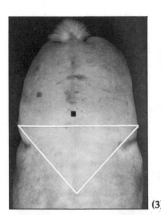

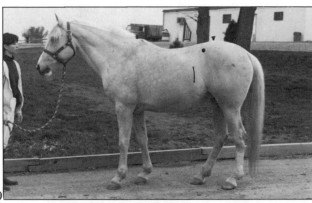

(3)

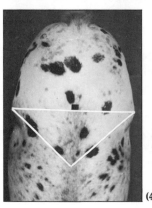

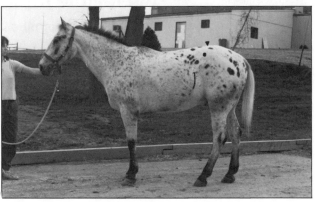

(4)

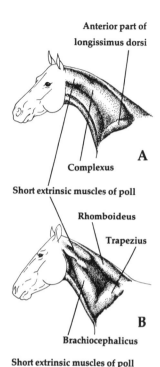

Anterior part of
longissimus dorsi

Complexus **A**

Short extrinsic muscles of poll

Rhomboideus

Trapezius

Brachiocephalicus **B**

Short extrinsic muscles of poll

Complexus

Trapezius

Brachiocephalicus **C**

Figure 6. Desirable and undesirable muscle development in the equine neck. A, ideal development; the complexus muscle dominates. B, a stiff-necked horse that pulls and throws his head up during transitions. Here the rhomboideus, trapezius, brachiocephalicus and short extrinsic muscles of the poll are all overdeveloped. C, pathological development in a horse with a dislocated atlanto-occipital joint (the joint between the skull and the first neck bone).

joint, her croup is also shorter than that of Horse #1, even though her pelvis and quarters are equally large. For these reasons, this mare is doubly disadvantaged: she lacks the lateral flexibility of Horses #1 and #2, while at the same time lacking the croup length and leverage of Horse #1 or #4. Moving the LS joint backward changes this mare from a potentially superb performer — a horse that should have been brilliant in collection — to one having only average capabilities.

Horse #4: Like Horse #3, this gelding shows a short back and a short, broad loin. However, because his LS joint is ideally located (top view), the profile of his topline in side view appears high, smooth and arched slightly upward like that of Horse #1. Although this gelding has neither as nice a neck nor as good a set of legs as Horse #3, he is the superior performer because the good placement of his LS joint shortens his lumbar span and lengthens his croup. This gives him the leverage he needs to shorten his underline and flex the LS joint for collected work.

Functional tradeoff: A short but level coupling like the Hungarian mare's is so strong that it's nearly indestructible, but horses with this structure can be stiff-backed. They usually trot better than they canter. A short but slightly peaked coupling like the half-Arab mare's is harder to preserve without pathology. However, horses possessing this construction tend to canter fluidly, with a supple loin.

The Back: Lab Exercise 2

The Telltale Topline

Years of use determine its shape

Conformation judges often speak of looking for the horse with a "smooth topline." But how smooth is smooth enough? Certainly, you wouldn't want a horse with the sort of topline you could lay a ruler on in side view: that kind of silhouette belongs on a beef steer. The horse's topline, in contrast, naturally forms a curving profile. But if the topline is "wavy," which of those curves is desirable? How much curve is acceptable?

The horse's topline is formed by the bones of the

Figure 7. The lump-hollow-lump characteristic of the rough-coupled horse. Ideally, the topline over the loin is high and convex, not concave and sagging. This structure predisposes the horse to muscular back strain.

spinal column and its overlying layers of ligamentous and muscular tissue. Ridden horses often acquire muscle strains in the lower back and enlargements of the bony pieces (vertebrae). Ligaments hold the chain of vertebrae together. If they tear, the bony pieces may not stay in perfect alignment. Likewise, abnormal or excessive development (hypertrophy) of the muscles along the topline makes the topline lumpy and can stiffen and reduce the movement of an otherwise flexible structure.

As you examine these four horses, check the topline of each for hollows that represent partial dislocations of vertebrae, dips that signal ligament tears, peaks formed by bony enlargements, and isolated, pillow-like bulges that indicate muscular hypertrophy.

Analysis

Horse #1: This horse possesses the best bone structure in the group, but he also has the lumpiest topline. This means that the soundness of his torso is not a sure bet — not nearly as good as that of his near-perfect set of legs.

The lumpiness in this topline arises entirely from muscular hypertrophy. This particular set of muscular bulges (Figure 6b) is characteristic of dressage horses that have been incorrectly schooled in devices which tie down the head (such as draw reins, standing martingale, chambon, de gogue, etc.) and which encourage them to strain upward. In actuality, strong and shapely muscles develop by alternately stretching and contracting which, like good gymnastic practice, will produce full, smooth topline muscling.

Horse #2: This mare has very good legs and pelvic structure. However, her back is "letting down," due to the gradual tearing of its ligaments at two key points — the withers and the point where the spine joins the croup (lumbosacral joint). The lump-hollow-lump at her coupling (Figure 7) is characteristic of muscle strain here. At least half of all ridden horses sooner or later acquire this trait, which, depending on its severity, diminishes the effectiveness which flexion of the joint (engagement of the hindquarters) has in raising the center of the back. Strengthening the horse's abdominal and iliopsoas muscles (Figure

8) act both as prevention and therapy for this condition.

Horse #3: This gelding shows "hatchet neck," a slash in the topline that results when the ligaments that bind the crest to the withers are torn. (Compare this nine-year-old to the 18-year-old gelding, who shows a dip but no "hatchet line.") This pathology can result from a bad fall, during which the horse slides on his face, or from the horse panicking and going over backwards while in a device that ties down the head. All such devices put pressure on the poll in order to bring about a lowering of the head.

This horse also shows a peaked enlargement of the dorsal spines of the first several lumbar vertebrae (Figure 9). Such an enlargement results either from repeated concussion (improper saddling and posting technique) or from moving or landing "hollow" so that the dorsal spines bump and grind together. The

(1) 18-year-old Thoroughbred gelding
(2) 20-year-old Thoroughbred mare
(3) 16-year-old Thoroughbred gelding
(4) 14-year-old Appaloosa gelding

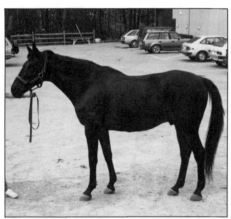

(1)

(2)

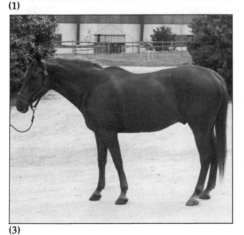

(3)

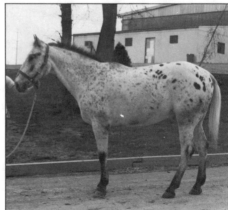

(4)

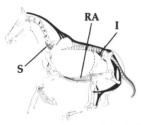

Figure 8. Bascule (arching) of the back and the neck-telescoping gesture are produced as the result of effort by the rectus abdominis, scalenus, and iliopsoas muscles, all of which lie below the vertebral column. The muscles above the vertebral column merely have to remain stretched and relaxed.

Figure 9. Peaked enlargement of the lumbar spines looks similar to the lump-hollow-lump characteristic of rough coupling (Figure 7), but in this case actual bony pathology is present. Consult your veterinarian to obtain a correct diagnosis.

shape of this horse's topline probably resulted from changes in his way of going subsequent to the neck injury.

Horse #4: High knees (long fore cannons) and somewhat slight bone in the front legs are this gelding's primary weaknesses. His nicely crested neck ties on to his prominent withers a bit low, forming a dip in the topline, but this is no cause for concern. Through his back and quarters, this horse's topline is smooth and strongly built. His back is as straight as it can be in side view and still be within the normal range for the equine species.

Functional tradeoff: Compare the 25-year-old Thoroughbred mare with the 18-year-old Appaloosa gelding. Which would you rather have — good legs or a good back? I would have liked to have owned the mare when she was younger, before the days and years of "little ligament tears" that add up to a low back at her age. On the basis of his back, the Appaloosa gelding rates slightly higher for durability, but the mare has the bone structure for greater speed and flexibility and is more harmoniously conformed.

The Back: Lab Exercise 3

Evaluating The "Transmission"

How the length of a horse's back determines the efficiency of his movements

In the standing horse, the free span of the back, measured from the highest point of the withers to the junction of the spine and croup (LS joint), serves to support the rib cage and to connect the fore- and hindquarters. But in the moving horse, it becomes something more: a dynamic transmission that functions to transfer the thrust or impulsion generated by the hindquarters to the forehand.

In the first two lab exercises, we've scrutinized the horse's back for anatomical signs of weak or damaged structure. Now it's time to look at overall back length and at proportions within the back, because these factors determine how efficiently a horse's back can function as a transmission.

Overall back length is determined by comparing it to total *body* length, measured in a straight line from the point of the shoulder to the point of the buttock

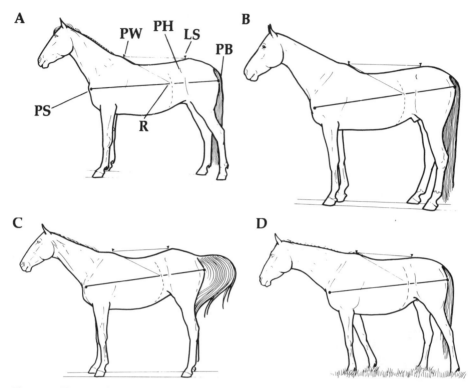

Figure 10. How to calculate the proportional length of a horse's back. First, measure the distance between the point of withers (PW) and the lumbosacral joint (LS) — this is the absolute length of the back. Secondly, measure the distance between the point of shoulder (PS) and the point of buttock (PB) — this is the total body length. Then calculate the proportional back length as follows:

Proportional Back Length = Back Length X 100 ÷ Body Length

Likewise, to calculate the proportional length of the rib cage, measure the length of the rib cage between the point of withers (PW) and the last rib (R). Then calculate the proportional length as follows:

Proportional Rib Cage Length = Rib Length X 100 ÷ Back Length

In the case of mare A and gelding B, who share very similar proportions despite a great difference in height, the back as a whole is too long (near 50% of body length) while the rib cage is too short (there is too much space between the last rib, marked by the dotted line, and the point of hip marked PH). Mare C is rough-coupled but has much better proportions; the whole length of her back equals 47% of her body length, and her rib cage carries well back to total 95% of her back length. Mare D not only has an ideally placed, smooth coupling, but has very desirable proportions: her back totals 47% of her body length while her rib cage equals 105% of her back (a percentage higher than 100 indicates that the rib cage is deep as well as long). Despite some limb faults, good axial body posture will be easy for this mare to maintain while being ridden and, as a result, she will be able to collect, extend and turn athletically.

(1)

(2)

Courtesy the author

(3)

(4)

(1) **24-year-old grade mare**
(2) **8-year-old German Warmblood gelding**
(3) **17-year-old Thoroughbred mare**
(4) **6-year-old Thoroughbred mare**

(Figure 10). Which horse pictured has the longest back? Does a good loin coupling shorten or lengthen the back span? Consider also the internal proportions of the torso. Which horse has the most space between the last rib and the point of hip?

Analysis

Horse #1: This mare's lumbosacral joint is placed far back, causing her to have a long back, a long loin and a short croup (see Figure 10a). This is a horse whose "transmission" is no more than a connector, even in movement.

This mare earns her keep by carting young hunter-seat riders over their first courses. She has survived because of a sturdy set of legs and a placid temperament. Her long back actually makes her good at her job: she jumps "flat," just stepping over fences. Her total lack of back flexion (bascule) wouldn't interest more advanced riders and prevents

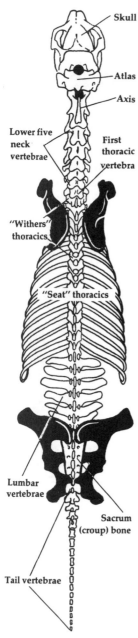

Skull

Atlas

Axis

Lower five
neck
vertebrae

First
thoracic
vertebra

"Withers"
thoracics

"Seat" thoracics

Lumbar
vertebrae

Sacrum
(croup) bone

Tail vertebrae

Figure 11. Bones of the horse's axial skeleton (the skull and vertebral column) seen in top view. The pectoral and pelvic girdles (shoulder blades and pelvis) are black.

her from succeeding at more demanding activities. The stillness of her back builds confidence in beginners who cannot keep their seat on a well-conformed horse whose back undulates up and down in movement.

Horse #2: This gelding is nothing more than an enlarged version of Horse #1 (Figure 10b). Like her, he has a long back, rather crooked hind legs and a short pelvis. He differs from her primarily in possessing a better loin coupling. As a result, he moves with a more elastic, undulating back. Because of his proportionally short pelvis, he isn't very powerful, and Horse #1 has legs with larger, cleaner joints and pasterns with better slope.

Horse #3: This mare's conformation is much nicer than either Horse #1 or Horse #2. Her lumbosacral joint is peaked and not ideally placed, but this is partly compensated for by a long pelvis which simultaneously lengthens the croup and greatly increases her thrusting power. Her overall back length is shorter than either #1 or #2, and the lumbar span within it is also short. The space between her last rib and the point of hip is ideal: not more than eight inches — a hand span (Figure 10c).

She stands over good legs, showing relatively little wear and tear. The left hind seems too smooth because it is stocked up, but this swelling, in her case a normal sign of age and stall confinement, should pass after a few minutes of free movement.

Horse #4: This is a mare with much the same torso as Horse #3's, and one thing more: a perfect lumbosacral joint. The reader who sent this photo asked whether the mare is suitable for competitive dressage, and the answer is a qualified "yes." Her excellent coupling guarantees that the impulsion generated by the hindquarters will be transmitted smoothly forward (Figure 10d). The mare is somewhat low withered, and her neck is also set somewhat low on her body. Her rider, therefore, will want to work her "long and low" — otherwise, the mare will learn to resist at the root of the neck, hollowing it there and blocking the flow of impulsion from back to front.

This mare's head is prettier than Horse #3, but her legs are not as good. She's slightly tied in below the knees in front — her flexor tendons appear to be too close to the cannon bones in those areas — and

Figure 12. Nicole Uphoff of West Germany and Rembrandt, a beautifully conformed, short-backed Warmblood gelding. The pair earned the gold medal in dressage at the 1988 Olympic Games in Seoul, South Korea.

cut out (narrow) under the hocks in back. Teaching her to move anatomically straight and developing a clear canter cadence will protect her somewhat vulnerable hocks in movements such as the pirouette, which might otherwise damage them by twisting.

Functional tradeoff: The internal proportions of the back are important. A long lumbar span (a long loin) weakens a back, no matter what the back's overall length. For this reason, Horse #2's back is stronger than Horse #1's. A long rib cage predisposes a horse for side-to-side (lateral) flexibility, while the lumbar span is almost incapable of lateral flexion (Figure 11). Thus Horses #3 and #4 are actually more capable of bending around turns than Horse #1 or #2. The argument that dressage horses should be long backed for flexibility is pure nonsense: a survey of nonexported European champions reveals that the best-structured backs tend to stay at home (Figure 12).

Of Mutton And The Mighty Camel

How the withers get their shape

Most of the "coffee table" books on equine conformation inform the reader that high withers are desirable in horses to keep the saddle from slipping to one side and from creeping too far forward. This is not, however, the most important function of the withers.

The ridge that riders call withers is composed of the long neural spines of the second through about the eighth to the twelfth thoracic vertebrae (Figure 13). The neural spines line up like the slats in a picket fence. The slats are not all of equal length, giving the withers their characteristic arched shape.

Besides being of different lengths, the neural "slats" lean backward. This braces them, like tent pegs, against the forward pull of the muscles and ligaments that form the crest of the neck. Thus, the withers serve two biomechanical functions: first, to anchor the neck and second, to provide a point of leverage, like a fulcrum, so that when the horse lowers and extends his neck, the center of his back rises. If the withers act as this kind of fulcrum, should they be high or low? Might their shape make a difference in function? Your answers to these questions will determine how you rate this set of examples.

Figure 13. Bones of the withers and their relationship to differently proportioned neck structures. A, "ewe neck" type 1, in which the lower curve of the neck bones is wide and deep, but the upper part of the neck (mitbah, or "turnover") is short. This makes the horse hammer-headed as well as ewe-necked. B, ewe neck type 2, which still shows the wide, deep lower cervical curve but also has a long upper curve. This type of ewe neck is harder for the untrained viewer to detect, especially if the crest of the neck blends nicely into high withers. C, a straight neck, in which neither cervical curve is very deep. The lower curve of the neck usually lies low on the neck in this type, but especially in certain bloodlines of American Quarter Horse, may lie higher. D, the ideal neck structure, in which the lower curve of the neck is shallow and lies high relative to the shoulder, and in which there is a long mitbah. This is the easiest neck to train.

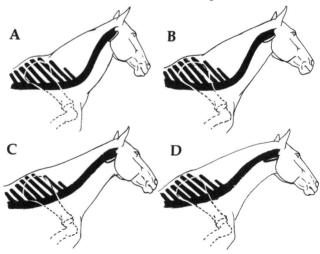

Analysis

Horse #1: This gelding is analyzed first because he has a beautiful neck and withers ideally conformed for a riding or sport horse. From such an example, the leverage role that the withers play in connecting the crest of the neck to the center of the back becomes obvious. The neck looks as if it springs from the center of the back. The neck attaches to the very top of the withers, and the withers are prolonged to the rear, smoothly blending into this horse's short back at nearly 50% of the distance from the point of shoulder to the loin coupling.

This gelding's faults are slight. His pelvis is a little short and steep and his "bone" a tad lighter than ideal. Overall, though, he is a beautiful example of an American Quarter Horse. This animal can do almost anything requiring toughness and athletic ability. He's a natural for cutting and stock work but could also be tried in reining or dressage, where his ability to pivot the forehand around the hindquarters, and his Andalusian-like nobility of carriage, would shine.

Horse #2: This mare has prominent withers, but the crest of her neck doesn't take advantage of them. This is not entirely because she was born with a "dip" in front of the withers. The muscular development of a horse's neck also depends upon the conformation of the back and loin coupling. Where the back and loin are as long as this mare's, the back tends to sag instead of rise under the rider's weight. A full or "double" back and crested neck do not develop in mares or geldings with sagging backs. A skillful rider who could effect engagement of the hindquarters (flexion of the lumbosacral joint) with the neck low and extended could fill in the "dip" and put a full crest on this neck. This is possible because the necessary bone structure is present. Because of her long back and loin, however, engagement of the quarters will always be more difficult for this mare than for Horse #1.

Horse #3: This stallion shows the same long back and loin as Horse #2 but has much poorer conformation in five other ways: a more peaked loin coupling; long, crooked hind legs that force him to stand rump-high and tip his balance to the front; and low (mutton) withers. The stallion also shows very light bone, and many structural weaknesses of the limbs — up-

Courtesy M. and C. Humphrey

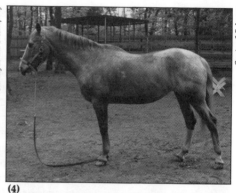

Courtesy S.E. Jansen

(3)

Courtesy J.L. Katz

(4)

Courtesy S. Purcell

(1) **Aged Quarter Horse gelding**
(2) **18-year-old Quarter Horse mare**
(3) **7-year-old Arabian stallion**
(4) **11-year-old Appaloosa-Thoroughbred gelding**

right pasterns, small round "knees" and hind cannon bones offset to the rear ("cut out under the hocks").

Because of his low withers, this stallion is limited in his ability to raise his back when he lowers and extends his head and neck. But with this loin, back and withers structure, why does this fellow have such a well-shaped neck? Every stallion develops a better-looking neck than he would have had as a gelding, partly as a secondary sexual characteristic, and partly as a result of the passage and piaffe-like movements that all stallions practice. Thus a pretty neck is no special distinction in a stallion, and in light of this horse's overall weak structure, his owners might seriously consider gelding him.

Horse #4: This gelding exemplifies "camel withers," the opposite of mutton withers. As in the case of Horse #2, excellent riding can do something to fill out the knife-thin crest of his neck and to raise the line of the crest to the top of the withers. However, camel withers drop off abruptly to the rear; even Horse #2's withers are prolonged farther to the rear than this fellow's.

Like Horse #3, this gelding has crooked hind legs and a poor loin coupling. His pelvic length is short, too. Nevertheless, he has enough bone, good feet and large, angular "knee" and hock joints, and these will go a long way toward keeping him sound through the period of training necessary to improve the shape of his neck and topline.

The Back: Lab Exercise 5

Ropes And Ladders

Building flexible, not rigid back muscles takes more than just good riding

Riding instructors are forever reminding their students that "dressage develops the horse's back." Yet from a biomechanical point of view, this statement is false. The muscles that such exercises as "striding up," turns and transitions really strengthen are not those of the back but the rectus abdominis of the horse's *belly* and the iliopsoas of the belly side of the back (Figure 8).

Desirable results for every riding discipline, including engagement of the hindquarters ("sticking his tail into the ground"), the neck-telescoping gesture ("going onto the bit" or "looking through the bridle") and the maintenance of bascule (a raised back or the weight-carrying posture), are effected by contractions of these muscles. Thus, the truest statement that a riding instructor can make is that "excellent riding strengthens the horse's underline."

What, then, about the back? When functioning normally, the longissimus dorsi muscles of the back (see Appendix A) act to *regulate* back movements and postures, but not to cause or *dictate* them. They perform their normal function by alternately stretching and contracting. In a horse that will not or cannot relax the large muscles of the back — paradoxical though it may seem — these muscles do not develop a full and rounded shape but instead become thin and flat and feel stiff or wiry. Thus, relaxation and stretching of the topline is more important in developing a full or "double" back than any technique that seeks directly to develop the back muscles.

When the back muscles fail to relax and are partially "on" all the time, the horse's back not only fails

Figure 14. Therapeutic exercise for horses can take many forms; these photos show several different, effective techniques. A, a 7-year-old American Quarter Horse showing tremendous impulsion and excellent overall body posture while being longed on one line. When used therapeutically, longeing is more than just a way to let a horse blow off steam. The beneficial effect of longeing is enhanced still more by the use of cavalletti. For more information on the proper use of cavalletti, see Reiner Klimke's "Cavalletti" (J.A. Allen, 1969) or Bertalan DeNemethy's "The DeNemethy Method" (Doubleday, 1988). B, the author longeing 21-year-old Arabian/Quarter Horse mare with two lines. This technique is a simple modification of line driving. The outside line, which goes from the left side of the horse's mouth, around her quarters and thence to the driver's left hand, simultaneously stimulates the mare to produce more engagement of the hindquarters while it keeps the quarters from deviating outward. C, the same mare at age 19 being longed over cavelletti. She is wearing a surcingle and longeing cavesson and, in (C), side reins. Poles can be used to lengthen the stride (C) or make it loftier (D). In C, the left hind leg carries all the weight for a split second. E, the author riding the same horse at a left-lead canter on a straight line while slowly flexing the mare's head left and right in rhythm with her gait. The head is held to the right for one or two strides before being straightened for a stride and then bent left. The mare responds easily to the request to flex laterally ("translate") at the poll; note

to fill out but becomes very stiff (abnormally high tonus) or even rigid, like a ladder. One quick way to stiffen a horse's back is to tie up his head and neck with a checkrein and then ask him to trot fast. This produces an efficient gait for horses involved in harness racing but does not promote an elastic ride. Another way to stiffen a horse's back is to tie his head *down* and ask him to trot fast. A third way is to tie the head in any position at all — up, down or to the side — for long periods of time (the "dumb jockey" approach).

As you assess these examples, look at the upper surface of each horse's rib cage. In which horses does this surface look hard, flat and angular? Such an appearance indicates a stiff back. Extra credit: three horses in this group are of the same breed. Which horses are they and what is the breed?

Analysis (page 29)

Horse #1: This young woman is clearly pleased with her 11-year-old Standardbred gelding. She writes to say that he was given to her after his career

A

B

the loose rein. To perform this exercise at the canter requires much gentle, persistent work. First attempts should be made at the halt; later, perfect the exercise at the walk and trot before trying it at the canter. F, just plain good riding can also make a world of difference. My heels could be farther back! Nevertheless, the mare carries me with generous impulsion. Good quality movement is evidenced by the wide "V" formed between the mare's two hind legs and her desirable axial body posture with neck-telescoping gesture and obvious engagement. The lively attitude of her tail is a cardinal sign of a relaxed and swinging back. Seeing this mare move, most people think she's a decade younger than she is.

as a racing trotter. The gelding has successfully learned to canter and has won some prizes at hunter competitions, all to his owner's credit. The photo, however, shows a classically undermuscled back. I hope his young owner will find the time for plenty of flat work with her equine companion and include the following simple exercises (Figure 14):

- leg yielding
- trotting and cantering a 20-meter circle, alternately flexing the horse's head and neck in and out
- walking six-meter circles and figure eights
- stretching the neck down and forward at trot and canter
- various forms of longeing.

All of these exercises will not only improve the quality of the gelding's canter, but will fill out his back.

The gelding has the Standardbred's typically good front legs and feet and excellent coupling. This individual is unusually straight in the hind limb for his breed, and this is what has made it easier for him to learn to canter. He also has an unusually long and well-formed neck for a Standardbred horse (#4's is

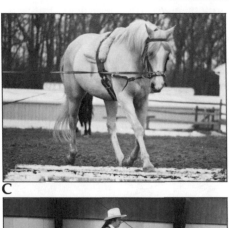

C

D

E

F

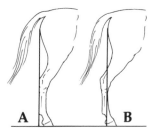

Figure 15. A perfect hind limb (A) compared to a crooked one (B). Depending on how the horse is posed, crooked hind limbs are also sometimes referred to as "overangulated," "camped out" or "sickle-hocked."

more typical), so that his new owner has had less of an uphill battle than others who try to help these horses have a second, mounted career.

Horse #2: This aged Standardbred gelding has the longest neck I've ever seen on a horse of his breed — so much so that one is tempted to think he's an American Saddlebred instead. Like Horse #1, this gelding also came from the harness track and shows the usual flat, angular, stringy back of a horse that has spent years trotting with his neck stiffly erect.

The job of making him into a riding horse will be harder than in Horse #1's case, because his pelvis is more level and his hind legs are more crooked, the hocks lying behind the buttocks when the hind cannon is vertical (Figure 15). Both these conformational features make it difficult for a horse's belly muscles to effect engagement of the hindquarters and consequent stretching of the back muscles. Cantering, by the way, is impossible unless the horse can coil the LS joint between canter strides.

Like Horse #1, this gelding has wonderful front legs and joints and an unusually nice shoulder. Trying the above-mentioned exercises with this fellow would certainly be a worthwhile project, but permanent changes in his musculature will probably not be confirmed for at least a year after beginning work.

Horse #3: The lighting in this photo of a seven-year-old Thoroughbred-Quarter Horse mare points up another characteristic of the stiff-backed horse: lacking fullness in the back muscles generally, there

Figure 16. A, with the rider tugging at the reins, this horse can't seem to get his hocks under his body. He moves forward faster and faster until he and his rider have lost control. B, this horse heads downhill by extending his neck and carrying his head a bit lower than the saddle horn. His rider helps — not hinders — his progress by leaning slightly forward.

(1)

Courtesy H. Kintz

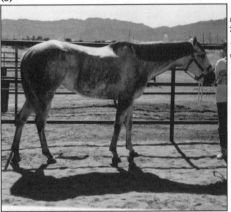

(2)

Courtesy E. Kilby

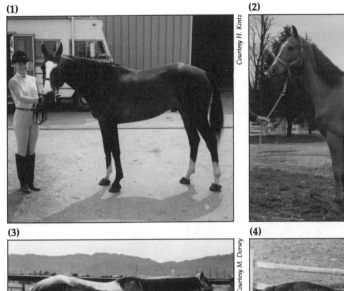

(3)

Courtesy M. Dorsey

(4)

Courtesy the author

(1) 11-year-old gelding
(2) Aged gelding
(3) 7-year-old mare
(4) 14-year-old mare

is a hollow behind and below the withers. This mare's coupling is the worst of the group, and as a consequence I see more evidence of low-back strain in her than in the others, i.e., a little more angularity in the surface over the loin and lumpiness in the top-line itself.

This mare has excellent hind legs, and doubt-lessly has always known how to canter. But when she canters, does she move freely in a bascule, bringing the inside hind leg well forward? Her knife-thin, un-crested neck and lack of fullness in her back make me suspect that she four-beats at the canter, shuffling along short strided; she probably picks up the canter by throwing her head back.

Her owner writes to ask whether she's suitable for endurance work. With care for her somewhat light front legs, the answer is yes, but this mare needs a year of arena work in addition to trail riding before competing. Endurance horses, like racing trotters, frequently develop a "ladder" back. This is caused by riding the trot indiscriminately over rolling terrain. The mare will benefit from the same exercises suggested for Horse #1. On the trail, trot her uphill and walk her down. Don't trot downhill until the horse can hold a bascule all the way down a steep grade at a walk (Figure 16). When the mare gets to the point that she doesn't rush or tumble forward as she approaches the bottom of the slope, she'll be ready to try trotting over terrain.

Horse #4: It's easy to pick faults in this 15-year-old Standardbred mare's conformation. She has an upright shoulder (exactly like Horse #3's), crooked hind legs (structured like Horse #2's, though posed differently), a long back and short, thick neck topped off by a hammer head. Her structurally good points are, however, functionally important: a close-to-perfect, short loin coupling, good length of croup and pelvis, and absolutely tremendous bone, short fore cannons, excellent joints and exemplary feet.

The photo conceals a particularly stiff back, which is just to point out that a photo does, sometimes, make a horse look better than he or she actually is. Since I happen to know this mare's history, I will share with you that she, too, came from the trotter track and when she first arrived at our barn, had a back that looked exactly like Horse #1's. Horse #4, however, could not canter and was so stiff that she

This mare is Horse #4, who appeared on page 29 in a 1985 snapshot. This photo was taken in 1987, after two years of steady practice of the exercises recommended above. She was also worked on the trail (but not trotted downhill).

fell down trying to turn a 20-meter circle at a trot. Her crest muscles (rhomboideus and trapezius) were so stiff that she could not stretch her neck down and forward. Her underneck was so thick and her poll so stiff that her "mouth" was like concrete. Her trot, too, was wooden, with no suspension and no hint of cadence.

All this was in the summer of 1985. The accompanying "after" photo shows this mare's appearance in August 1987, after two years of exercises. The mare can now canter, trots elastically in a bascule and goes readily forward from the leg to the bit. She has a second life as an all-around pleasure and trail horse, and an owner who takes as much delight in her daily progress as in looking forward to their first appearance before a dressage judge. 'Nuff said?

The Back: Lab Exercise 6

When The Ring Of Muscles Breaks Down

Understanding the source of a horse's structural sags and bags

The relationships between the horse's back, belly, loins and neck are the product both of conformation and habits of movement. This chapter's photos have been chosen to enhance your understanding of the all-important "ring of muscles," the chain of bony as well as muscular and ligamentous structures that allow the horse to move with unrestricted agility while burdened with weight from above.

As you glance over each of these examples, focus on the shape of the horse's abdomen. Is there a relationship between how stretched and sagging a horse's belly is and the shape of his topline? What happens to the shape of a horse's neck after his belly and back begin to sag? Does the slope of the pelvic bones depend on abdominal fitness?

Analysis

Horse #1: I chose this equine senior citizen not to criticize her conformation after a long life of service, but because she shows the muscular development of a horse whose ring of muscles no longer functions.

This horse's breakdown probably began with strain of the muscles overpassing the loins and lumbosacral joint. Stretching of the loin ligaments and straining of its muscles made this mare adopt a defensive habit of continual low-level "clamping" of the back muscles, resulting in the characteristic *flat, shiny* look of a "dead" back — one that has become very stiff or even rigid like a ladder. This habit of back rigidity in turn made it difficult for her to effectively contract her belly muscles. Eventually she lost all tone there, resulting in a potbelly. When the mare's abdominal tone fell below a certain level, her back also began to sink behind the withers. At the same time, her pelvis became more horizontal and her stifle joints more open. Then she began to have trouble cantering, and began to carry her neck nearly vertical at the trot, resulting in overdevelopment of the rhomboideus muscles of the neck (see Appendix A).

Horse #2: This gelding is in regular work under skillful, knowledgeable riders. Thus, although he, too, has a stretched loin and sagging back, the muscular strain is less and irregularities in his body out-

(1) 32-year-old grade mare
(2) 12-year-old Lipizzan-cross gelding
(3) 19-year-old Morgan gelding
(4) 13-year-old half-Arabian gelding

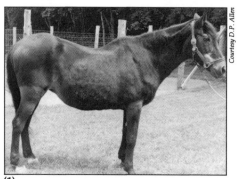

(1)

(2)

(3)

(4)

line and muscular development are less evident. Still fairly obvious is the fact that his neck sags rather than arches at the root, but his fit underline saves him most pain and dysfunction. Note the smooth, level profile of his underline and the vertical depth from loin to groin.

Horse #3: Conformation can predispose a horse for a lifetime of harmonious function or to athletic mediocrity. This fellow is very long in the back (remember that a horse's back extends all the way from the peak of the withers to the peak of the croup). As a result, he needs absolutely tremendous fitness and strength to move with engagement, bascule, lightness and impulsion.

Except for being tied in below the knees, he appears to have good legs and feet. Because this gelding has difficulty producing suspension or cadence, he is a guaranteed comfortable ride; there's little work for a rider when the horse executes a "stepping trot." In fact, it wouldn't surprise me at all if this fellow could produce a nice fox trot or running walk.

Conformation produces habits of movement, and habits of movement in turn produce characteristic muscular development. The reason this gelding's neck is so cresty is not due to his breeding as much as to the fact that — like Horse #1 — his "ring" isn't fully functional. I believe, however, that with proper conditioning and riding, any horse can produce springy, suspended gaits.

Horse #4: Now that you can identify the characteristic look of a horse with a partly or wholly non-functioning "ring," do you just retire or pass up horses with this problem? If you're a competitor and feel you must win, the answer to that is "yes." If, however, you're interested in horse training — that is, in developing a horse's weight-carrying and athletic abilities to their fullest capacities, read on.

There is essentially nothing wrong with this gelding's bone structure. He has a long, well-shaped neck, a well-placed coupling, a medium-length back with short loins, good length and depth of quarters and excellent feet. He's a bit rump-high, but his biggest problem is that he needs "belly therapy" *now*, before his lumbosacral joint and loins become damaged. Longeing over cavalletti (Figure 14) is the most effective technique I know for strengthening a horse's abdominal muscles and improving "ring" function.

Figure 17. This relatively short-necked pony has no trouble flexing his neck to curve around the barrel. In equine necks, short does not equal stiff.

Chapter 2

How To Look At A Horse's Neck

Of length, balance and the paradox of flexibility

By beginning with the horse's back, we have literally chosen to start studying conformation from the horse's "center." Branching outward from the horse's trunk are five parts which function as major appendages: the four limbs and the neck.

Anatomically speaking, the neck is the forward continuation of the vertebral column which also structures the horse's back. Unlike the bones of the back, however, the neck bones are unencumbered by ribs. Because of this and because of the unique designs of the individual neck bones, the neck is the most flexible of the horse's appendages.

Length, Flexibility and Balance

Almost all species of mammals have the same number of bones (seven) in their neck. It may come as a surprise to discover that the very long neck of the giraffe and the camel, and the long neck of the horse, as well as the shorter necks of cattle, dogs, pigs, cats and people are all supported by the same number of neck bones. Whether in nature or in the context of selective breeding under domestication, to make a longer neck means to make the individual neck bones longer, not more numerous.

This fact leads to insight as to the true functional capabilities of long vs. short necks. Horses with very short necks rarely have thin ones, but contrary to popular mythology, despite their bulk, such necks usually remain flexible: just think of the average 4-H or Pony Club "games" pony, who has no trouble zipping around flags, poles or barrels (Figure 17). Close-up photos of gymkhana horses and ponies show that even short-necked specimens curve their necks as they pass at speed around obstacles. At the opposite extreme are horses with very long necks which are often thin, poorly muscled and stiff. Long-necked horses have several physical "strategies" at their disposal to resist curving their necks in the direction of the desired turn under saddle (Figure 18). At first glance it would appear that the long-necked horse, who is more attractive to look at, would have the more flexible neck, but this is not so. Why?

Flexibility depends upon the horse's ability to bend his neck at each of his joints. Given seven bones in the neck, there are eight joints, of which seven will permit lateral and longitudinal bending. All side-to-side and arching movements in a horse's neck must occur at one or more of these joints.

Let's imagine one horse with a neck seven feet long, and another one of the same height with a neck 3½ feet long. On average, the long-necked horse has one joint for every foot of neck length. The short-necked horse has one every six inches. Because he possesses twice as many joints per foot of neck length, the short-necked horse has a neck with *twice* the potential flexibility of the long-necked horse!

The horse species has been domesticated for five thousand years and, from the very beginning, in every European, Asian and American horse culture, breeders strived to select and breed horses with necks longer than the original wild bloodstock. This is because the neck has a second important function to perform: it is the horse's major balancing organ, a sort of oar which he can throw to the side or up or down to compensate for shifts in the balance of limbs or torso during turning, stopping, climbing or jumping. While the big cats use their thick tails for this, the horse uses his neck.

The purpose of breeding horses with longer

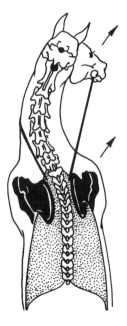

Figure 18. The lateral S-bend is a resistance that comes naturally to the stiff-necked, long-necked horse. In this scenario, the rider approaches a corner of the arena and pulls back on the right rein to induce the horse to turn right, following the track. Instead of allowing the bones of his neck and thorax to flow smoothly around the turn like boxcars in a toy train, the horse faces right but also leans right and leads right with his right shoulder, producing the lateral S-bend. The cure? The rider should (1) shift to an opening rein, taking the right rein well away from the neck; (2) release with the left rein, permitting the left shoulder space to move left; and (3) kick (with the right heel) or slap (with reins, romal or bat) the horse's right shoulder, to induce him to displace weight from the right shoulder to the left one.

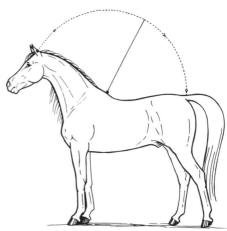

Figure 19. The "long-necked" show horse of this turn-of-the-century photograph doesn't look particularly long-necked by today's standards. Fashions in conformation may change — but our idea of how a good quality horse is built should not. A little more neck length would not have hurt this fellow, but at most he should conform to the proportions shown in Figure 20.

Figure 20. This top-quality Arabian stallion demonstrates the maximum neck length for athletic performance. Necks that exceed the body length tend to be stiff (see Figure 18) and add nothing to mounted balance. This individual was a champion eventer in Europe, on one occasion beating a field of 14 Thoroughbreds. After importation to the U.S., he became a champion "park" horse.

necks is to produce athletic horses who can turn, stop, climb and jump even while carrying the burden of a rider. But as we have seen, extremes in neck length trade off against flexibility. I once heard an experienced conformation judge declare: "You can't bring me a Quarter Horse with too long a neck." He then used the example of the circus tightrope walker, who uses a long pole to balance himself, just as a horse uses his neck to balance himself. No tightrope walker uses a 3½-foot-long pole; that's too short to be useful. But equally disastrous would be the use of a 200-foot-long pole! The big cat's tail is neither bobbed nor so long that it drags on the ground while he runs.

Unfortunately today there are many horses whose necks are at — or beyond — the upper limit of usefulness in balance and well into the range of absolute length which promotes stiffness and resistance to turning. Today's fashion — not function — calls for such long necks. Our idea of "long" has gotten longer and longer over time; the long-necked horse of only 80 years ago (Figure 19) would be considered medium- to short-necked today.

Considering all the functional tradeoffs, what is the best length for a horse's neck? Figure 20 shows how to "see" the ideal neck length. A neck of good length harmonizes with body build as a whole, giving an impression of overall balance.

Shape

Thus far, we have considered the bones of the

Figure 21. The S-shaped internal chain of neck bones does not follow the horse's crest.

horse's neck as if they were spools of uniform shape. However, each and every neck bone has a different shape. The differently shaped articulations between neck bones cause the bones to fit together to form an S-shaped chain. However, the crest of the horse's neck does not follow the curve of his bones (Figure 21); that's why a horse's neck does not look like that of a goose, deer or camel, whose necks exactly parallel their curved internal structure.

Because of the superadded crest, the S-shape within a horse's neck is harder to see than in uncrested animals but by no means impossible. The proportions of the upper, middle and lower curves of the vertebral S determine the shape of the neck which is visible from the outside. The following chart shows how the internal S dictates familiar variations in external form:

Some Common Neck Forms And Their Functions

Description Of Internal "S"	External Form	How It Functions
Short upper curve Medium middle segment Long, deep lower curve	Short upper curve produces "wrong," "hammer-headed," abrupt attachment of head to neck and acute angle at throatlatch. Long, deep lower curve produces external appearance variously termed "ewe neck," "upside-down neck," "hollow crest" or "fallen crest"	Horse tends to carry head too high or "stargaze;" note that a neck that is too *low* at the root produces head carriage that is too *high*. Hard to get horse to lower head and stretch neck forward for suppling or correct transitions. Muscle development thin and hard above, too thick on underside
Medium upper curve Medium to long middle segment Long, deep lower curve	"Common neck" or "rubber neck." Its appearance is similar to the above, but the neck is less upright and may be longer; the angle at the throatlatch is more open	Similar to above, although head may not be carried as high. In heavy-bodied individuals, the neck may have a heavy, ungainly or "rubbery" feel when bitted. This is the horse most likely to learn how to overflex his neck and "run through his shoulder"
Medium to long upper curve Medium to long middle segment Short, shallow lower curve	Neck goes "straight out the front" or appears horizontal; the horse has a build like the Greek letter "Pi" — two legs supporting a long horizontal bar (the torso and neck) on top	Ideal structure in a stock, endurance, race, three-day event, hunter or polo horse. Efficient, athletic; bridles and supples easily. Horse does not "stargaze," "run through his shoulder" or "ball up"
Medium to long upper curve Medium middle segment Short, shallow lower curve	"Arched neck" or "turned-over neck"	Ideal structure in a dressage, bullfight, reining, park, parade horse or a jumper. Showy without loss of athleticism; bridles and supples easily. Horse does not "stargaze" or "run through his shoulder," but may "ball up" (curl his neck down until his nose is pressing against his chest)

As the chart above makes clear, horses' necks come in all shapes; any combination of short, medium or long in any of the three segments of the vertebral S is possible. However, the most important part of the neck from a functional standpoint is the shape of the lower curve. If the lower curve is short and shallow — in other words, if the base of the neck is set high on the chest — the horse will be easy to train and ride, even if he also happens to be hammer-headed. If the neck is set low on the chest, as in the ewe-necked horse, training becomes much more difficult even if the head happens to be set on well. The upper curve, mitbah or "turnover" area of the neck is second in importance to the root. The longer the upper curve, the better the head is likely to be set on the neck, and the cleaner and more open the throatlatch area will be.

The Neck-Telescoping Gesture

To understand why the lower curve of the neck is more important from the standpoint of training and function than the upper curve, horsemen must understand what physical movements the horse makes with his neck when he is said to "go onto the bit," to "look through the bridle" or to "stretch to the bit." Most training manuals emphasize the necessity of inducing a horse to "release" or "yield" or "flex" at the poll, thus making a "yes" gesture with the head, bringing the forehead nearer to the vertical and closing the angle at the throatlatch. While this movement is necessary for good equitation, it is governed by the neck-telescoping gesture that originates not close to the poll but at the *root* of the neck.

Although the neck-telescoping gesture is rarely mentioned in the equestrian literature (the best description is by the French master General De Carpentry), it is easy to understand how it works, since people can also make this gesture. Sit comfortably in a chair or in your saddle, with your weight squarely on your seat bones. Shrug your shoulders several times to relax them; be sure you aren't holding them up in an endless shrug. Look straight ahead. Now, make your neck longer — push your head straight upward toward the ceiling. That's the neck-telescoping gesture made by the human physique. When a horse

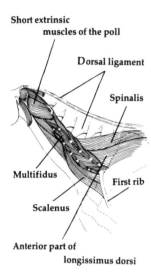

Short extrinsic muscles of the poll

Dorsal ligament

Spinalis

Multifidus

First rib

Scalenus

Anterior part of longissimus dorsi

Figure 22. Deep dissection of the horse's neck, showing the scalenus and other muscles that effect the neck-telescoping gesture. Contraction of the left and right scaleni flattens out the lower curve of the horse's neck and tends to push the neck bones upward. These movements are aided by simultaneous contraction of the spinalis and anterior part of the longissimus dorsi muscles. When these three muscles contract, the rider feels that the horse's neck and rib cage suddenly become "all of one piece." The multifidus muscle and the overlying complexus muscle (not shown here) are composed of many short slips that "lace" the separate neck bones together. During the neck-telescoping gesture, these muscles fill with blood and bulge.

produces the same gesture, he makes the same movement with his neck, except that his forehead is pushed forward, not upward. This is because the equine neck lies in the horizontal plane, not the vertical plane like ours (Figure 14f).

People and horses can both produce a neck-telescoping gesture because the neck bones of both species curve at the base. It is not actually possible for muscles to directly push your head up or the horse's head forward; an important rule of physiology states that *muscles don't push*. When a muscle does anything, it contracts or gets shorter. When you make a neck-telescoping gesture, you make it because specific muscles in the base of your neck contract. But if muscles contract, how in the world can your head go *up*? If the same mechanism operates in the horse, how can contraction *lengthen* a horse's neck?

The neck-telescoping gesture works because the scalenus muscles, which lie close to the underside of the bones forming the lower curve of the neck, act to *flatten out* this curve when they contract (Figure 22). Straightening out the lower curve of the neck is much easier if the lower curve is already short and shallow; that's why horses with this build have the advantage over ewe-necked ones. However, the scaleni can be strengthened through proper therapeutic exercise in any horse, no matter what his build. By teaching and training this gesture, the appearance and function of almost any horse's neck can be greatly improved.

Since the scalenus muscles lie deep within the neck of the horse, down next to the bones, their action cannot be directly seen or felt from the outside. However, the neck-telescoping gesture produces three effects easily seen from the outside:

1) It *raises the root of the horse's neck*, making the lower third of the crest fill up and rise higher relative to the top of the withers (Figure 23b,d,f);

2) It pushes the horse's forehead away from its chest. The reins of a "green" horse with weak scaleni must either be loose or instantaneously lengthened in order to permit the gesture;

3) It causes the complexus muscle of the horse's neck to bulge and become visible. Prolonged practice of this gesture will bring the bulging lower edge of the complexus all the way down to the level of the horse's shoulder, completely "remodeling" the shape of the neck (Figure 14f).

Figure 23. External effects of the neck-telescoping gesture demonstrated by horses participating in three of the four major American riding disciplines. A and B are "saddle-seat" horses, and could be American Saddlebreds, Arabians, Morgans or National Show Horses competing in a park, three-gaited, English Pleasure or five-gaited class. Horse A is not making a neck-telescoping gesture; in fact, he is "sucking the root of his neck down," which he accomplishes by contracting his brachiocephalicus, rhomboideus and trapezius muscles, which bulge as a consequence. Saddle-seat specialists refer to this horse as "elk-necked." Horse B exemplifies the ideal; he neither leans over his right front leg nor pulls at the bit. As a bonus, he also has higher, more brilliant knee "action." C and D are dressage horses, and could be of any breed competing at any level. Lacking the strength to make a neck-telescoping gesture, horse C lies on the bit, hollows his neck, raises his head, jams his shoulders, leans over his right front leg and "flicks" the extended left fore hoof. Horse D exemplifies the ideal. The toe of the extended forefoot should point down toward the ground and should not extend farther forward than the projection of the plane of the horse's forehead. E and F represent "stock-seat" horses, and could be of any breed. In addition to lacking a neck-telescoping gesture, horse E shows a "broken neck," which indicates that he does not flex at the poll joint. Horse F exemplifies the ideal. This horse can be stopped from a dead run by aids of the seat alone, because he has the strength to

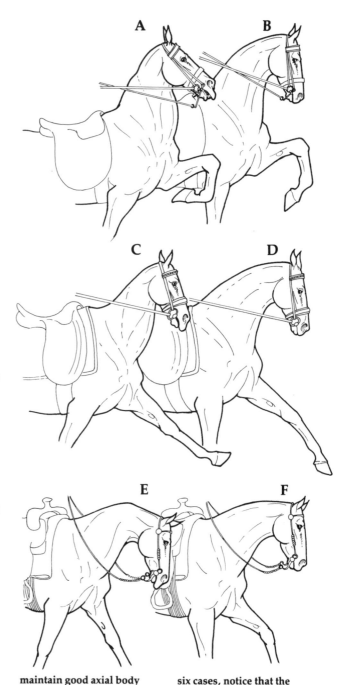

maintain good axial body posture, and therefore has good balance. In such a case, there is never a need to hang onto the bridle reins. In all six cases, notice that the desirable or undesirable action of the forelimbs is the RESULT of the axial body posture.

Figure 24. "Showing the horse the way to the ground" — doorway to higher levels of performance. The horse cannot do this and will not respond this way to the action of the snaffle bit and reins until he can make a neck-telescoping gesture.

There are two forms of the neck-telescoping gesture: elementary or gravity-aided, and advanced or anti-gravity. Correct therapeutic "stretching" to the bit — the way most horses should be ridden most of the time — involves the elementary neck-telescoping gesture. To make this gesture yourself, first make your neck longer as you did before. While still actively lengthening your neck, tip forward, allowing gravity to gently pull your head forward and downward. You will feel a strong stretching not only in the back of your neck, but extending down the center of your back past your shoulder blades. The stretching sensation produced this way is much stronger, and different in quality, than if you simply relaxed your neck and let it hang forward. This is why the very low, "peanut-roller" head and neck position sometimes adopted by Western pleasure horses is no indication of athletic achievement; relaxation and a low head carriage without the neck-telescoping gesture enhance neither a horse's appearance nor his performance ability.

In dressage parlance, "showing the horse the way to the ground" (Figure 24) *presupposes* the neck-telescoping gesture. In this exercise, the reins are neither released nor lengthened. Rather, the horse has sufficient strength in the scaleni to first raise the root of its neck and then, while maintaining the effort, to stretch down and forward. The horse does not lean on the snaffle bit — he pivots his mouth around it. The ability to perform this exercise is the doorway to higher levels of performance.

The advanced, anti-gravity form of the neck-telescoping gesture is the one you perform if you simply lengthen your neck straight upward against the pull of gravity. This form of the gesture is much harder for a horse than for a person: great strength in the scalenus muscles, developed from long conditioning which also stretches the muscles along the top of the crest is required before a horse can push his neck straight upward from the root (Figure 25). As explained in Chapter 3 of Volume I (pp. 56-57), collection of the form required for success in upper-level dressage, reining, park and three-gaited work requires that the horse be able to make the advanced neck-telescoping gesture. For example, the upper-level dressage movement called *passage* is impossible unless the horse first is able to make a very strong

A   B

Figure 25. These two photos show the essential similarity of dressage and reining. A, U.S. Olympic team member Jessica Ransehousen and Orpheus executing flying tempe changes during the 1988 selection trials. Orpheus takes up the rein because he seeks the bit through engagement of the hindquarters, bascule of the back and the neck-telescoping gesture. B, Dick Waltenberry beautifully slides to a stop on The Material Girl, who shows the same cardinal signs of collection as the dressage horse. Notice the bulging complexus muscle in the neck of each.

neck-telescoping gesture of this advanced type.

As the anti-gravity neck-telescoping gesture raises the root of the neck, it benefits the function of the neck's upper curve as well. When collection is achieved this way, the neck-telescoping gesture acts to *open* the throatlatch, even if the horse's forehead is held in the vertical plane (Figure 26). Opening the throatlatch opens the horse's windpipe and frees his voice box (larynx) and assures that there will be plenty of space for the base of the tongue, even if he is performing in high collection. If collection instead is forced by merely pulling the horse's head back so that the forehead comes into the vertical plane, the excessive flexion at the poll that this causes (Figure 23a,c,e) will close the throatlatch, crushing the muscles of the lower surface of the neck up into the ganache. This constricts the horse's breathing, making it sound raspy, and painfully crushes the voice box up against the root of the tongue. The tongue then seeks to find space in the only place remaining — outside the lips.

The cure for a hanging tongue, therefore, does not lie in a tongue-tie, but in inducing *and allowing* the horse to make a neck-telescoping gesture. Since this is not a book on training, little will be said here about how the rider is to induce the horse to contract the scaleni, except to note that tight reins will prevent the horse from making the gesture, especially in the beginning of training, when the scaleni are weaker than an average man's arms. Horses naturally offer the neck-telescoping gesture in response to squeezes of

A

B

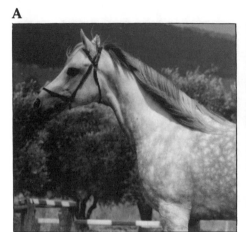 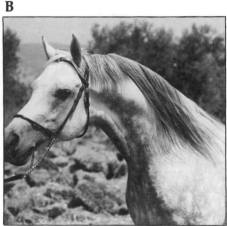

Figure 26. This stallion shows what a horse looks like before (A) and after (B) he makes the neck-telescoping gesture. Stallions naturally produce the gesture when they smell a mare, but the ridden horse also produces it in response to squeezes of the rider's calf.

the rider's calf, so long as they are ridden either on loose reins (American Western style) or with a "following" hand, which knows how to yield the instant the gesture is offered.

Applying these new concepts of neck function will enhance not only your ability as a rider and trainer but also your eye for a good neck. In the next exercise, you're invited to practice spotting the "easy to train" neck — the one that just naturally wants to make the neck-telescoping gesture.

THE NECK: LAB EXERCISE 1

A Menagerie Of Necks

How the chain of vertebrae determines the structure's shape

The most important fact to know about a horse's neck is the precise shape of the bone structure supporting it. Whether your horse has a "ewe," "swan" or "bull" neck or something in between is largely determined by the proportions of the neck's internal "S" (Figure 21).

To assess the size and shape of the important lower curve, first check the point at which the base of the throat enters the horse's chest. Next look for the widest point in the lower half of the horse's neck. Are these points located low or high relative to the chest?

Muscular development also can be a giveaway, but don't be fooled by length; a short neck can be just as well-shaped as a long one.

Analysis

Horse #1: This is a classic example of a "swan neck": long, slender and shapely. Its shapeliness does not derive from an excess of length but from the most desirable internal bone structure. The lower curve of the S is short, shallow and placed very high (higher than halfway up the line of the shoulder). There is also a long upper curve or mitbah. Structurally, the only changes that might benefit this horse would be a shorter back and a stronger loin coupling. The hind legs are a bit crooked, but all four legs, all the joints and the hooves are well structured.

Delicately beautiful, this fellow is especially suitable as a lady's horse — especially a lady with very light hands. Every conformational feature is a trade-

(1) 8-year-old Anglo-Arab mare
(2) 4-year-old Thoroughbred gelding
(3) 13-year-old Quarter Horse gelding
(4) 12-year-old Palomino mare

(1)   Courtesy M. Herald

(2)   Courtesy Col. D. Deane-Freeman

(3)   Courtesy S. McGuffigan

(4)   Courtesy C. Desina

Figure 27. Reins attached to a non-leverage bit, such as the snaffle, can act as a crutch for the scalenus muscles only when they pass level with or below the lower curve formed by the neck bones. If they are adjusted higher, the green horse will merely drape his neck in the reins like a vulture. With training, as the short extrinsic muscles of the poll (SEP) and other muscles of the topline become loose and supple, and as the scalenus gains strength, the reins can be fixed at position A and the horse will still be able to make a neck-telescoping gesture. Higher rein positions are justified to the extent that scalenus contraction is capable of raising the root of the horse's neck.

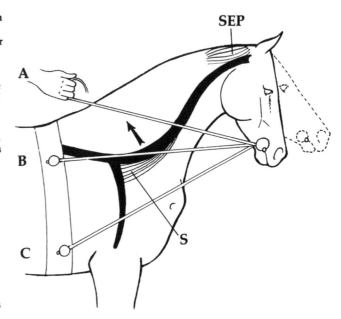

off, and a perfect neck is no exception. Horses structured like this are easy to put "on the bit" — but all too easily they can learn to roll their noses down to touch their chests, evading contact by getting behind or under it. With careful, intelligent handling, this fellow will be a winner in hunter, hunter-hack, dressage, or even Western pleasure.

Horse #2: Like many of his relatives at the racetrack, this fellow is ewe-necked and hammer-headed. Otherwise his conformation is good, especially for hunter competition. He has exceptionally good hindquarters and his slightly upright shoulder will actually help him to fold well over fences. The fore pasterns are as long as they well can be but appear upright only because of the pose.

The opposite of Horse #1 in neck conformation, this gelding has no mitbah and a lower curve that is long, low and deep. Although ewe neck results from a low placement of the lower S-curve, many people erroneously think that these horses have their necks "set on high" because they tend to *carry* their heads high. Ewe-necked horses almost always stargaze, poking their noses up and out and getting above or over the bit.

Snaffle-bit contact can be used successfully to train a green horse only when the line formed by the reins cuts level with or below the lower S-curve (Figure 27). If the reins pass above the curve, contact merely induces the horse to drape his neck on the rider's hands — something like trying to rein a vulture. The purist who tries to train this horse might wish she were an orangutan until the horse gains enough strength to carry his head lower and the root of his neck higher. Meanwhile, longeing with side reins attached low on the girth, while working the horse through many transitions, will help.

Horse #3: In contrast to the two horses just discussed, this is a classic example of a short, "bull" neck. Internally, this fellow's neck bones form a wide, deep lower curve, but a very short upper curve. The base of the lower curve (the widest part of the neck from side to side) lies much lower than halfway up the line of the shoulder. Internally and externally, therefore, this neck is the opposite of Horse #1's. While this type of neck is unattractive, as discussed in Chapter 2, it is incorrect to assume that it will be stiff. Its disadvantage does not lie in stiffness, but in the fact that such a short neck cannot act effectively as a counterbalance to the mounted torso.

Horse #4: This example is a "fooler," for here is a mare with nearly as good a bony neck structure as Horse #1, the only difference being one of overall length. She certainly is not bull-necked like Horse #3. However, like Horse #3, this mare's thick lower neck muscles reveal that she pokes her nose out and leans or pulls on the reins. To cure this, and at the same time improve the neck's appearance, I recommend that her rider try a mild snaffle or rubber mullen-mouth bit with no leverage properties. Then it would be best for the rider to take her courage in her teeth, and drop the contact — ride "on the buckle" at a slow jog trot, gradually taking up light contact again as the mare finds her balance in a jog.

The thick rhomboideus muscle developed along the mare's crest shows that she needs to stretch her topline; she probably has to spread her legs far apart to get her nose down to graze. Her rider can teach her to stretch her neck down at a jog trot by first establishing light contact, then bumping or hugging her with her legs as she gradually feeds the rein out. The game is to get the mare to "follow the bit down." Later, she can learn "the way to the ground" (Figure 24). At least five minutes of stretching near the beginning and at the end of every ride would be beneficial.

This mare has a good back, loin, quarters and exceptionally good pelvis. Her hamstrings tie on high and her gaskin is a tad long compared to Horse #1 and Horse #3, indicating that she'll tend to move with short, rapid hind strides. Her rider will need to teach her to obey a slow rate of posting to counteract this tendency.

The trade-off between lower S-curve height and a tendency to get behind the bit has already been mentioned. The equivalent trade-off for the horse with a low-placed lower S-curve is speed at the racetrack, where horses are taught to pull against the rein and where the very act of galloping tends to flatten and raise that loopy lower neck. Animals like Horse #1 tend to float up in front when they gallop. This is considered beautiful in the dressage arena, but it does not predispose to speed.

THE NECK: LAB EXERCISE 2

The Long And Short Of Equine Necks

In the final analysis, shape is more important than length

A horse's neck is, perhaps, the most obvious feature of his conformation. Even those who are new to horsemanship will have little difficulty in telling which of this month's examples have long necks. While shape is more important than length, there is still such a thing as a neck that is too long and fine.

In each of these examples, the horse's neck ties into the withers well, each animal has normal neck muscling, and each torso shows evidence of a functioning "ring of muscles" (see Volume 1, Chapter 3). Yet one of these horses has a longer, weaker loin, a shallower groin and less powerful hind limb muscles, and as a result, a weaker "ring."

Analysis

Horse #1: This good-quality Thoroughbred gelding has had a history of injuries to the deep layers of the skin of his back and to the hamstring muscles (those that run from the point of the buttock down toward the hock). Though these structures are not major components of "ring" function, the damage to them has acted to diminish somewhat the horse's otherwise very high potential. He's not quite as deep from loin to groin and not quite as smooth behind the withers and over the croup as he could be.

He does, however, have a beautiful neck and head (tongue and all). The neck has a straight shape at rest, narrow at the base, but shows no muscular maldevelopment due to his owner's sound training techniques, which include lots of hill work. As a result of the effort over physically challenging terrain, the gelding has well-rounded quarters with a nicely balanced development of the protractor muscles (the mass between the stifle and point of hip) and the hamstrings. Additionally, the gelding's slightly toed-

(1) 13-year-old Thoroughbred gelding
(2) 2-year-old Appaloosa gelding
(3) 9-year-old Tennessee Walker-Quarter Horse gelding
(4) 7-year-old American Saddlebred mare

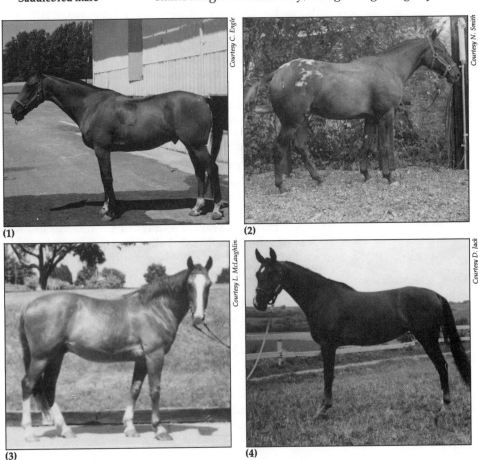

Courtesy C. Engle

Courtesy N. Smith

(1)

(2)

Courtesy L. McLaughlin

Courtesy D. Jack

(3)

(4)

in stance in front is a functional advantage and acts to compensate for his high "knees."

Horse #2: This gelding is only two years old but he looks older to me; I would have guessed that he is six. Despite his mature outward appearance, however, internally his bones and joints are far from fully grown. They won't be completely developed until he reaches the age of five to eight years, and the last to mature will be the intervertebral joints — those we sit upon when we ride. For this reason, I strongly discourage riding two-year-olds. Early riding has two pernicious effects: it shortens the horse's potential life span and induces an early, subtle habit of defensive "back clamping."

This gelding has a short but beautifully shaped neck. His pelvic angle is steep, but there's plenty of length from the point of the hip to the point of the buttock. His torso is absolutely fabulous. With his strong hocks and short gaskins, this fellow would make a terrific reining prospect.

His one major flaw, however, is "calf knee" (see p. 85 of this book). As a result, I recommend *not* jumping him and keeping his front heels fairly high. That way, his owner will minimize the chances of carpal arthritis which can be the result of this structural fault.

Horse #3: In a letter accompanying this photo, this gelding's owner states: "I was concerned about the lump in his loin area when I bought him, but his temperament was so sweet I decided to take a chance on him. I'm glad I did! It turns out the animal has a lovely running walk...he runs barrels...jumps to four feet (my limit, not his), babysits children and at the end of a three-hour ride, begs for more. The moral of my story is, he may be odd-looking, but the horse is a winner!"

My question is — what lump in the loin area? The gelding has a short, strong, smooth coupling flanked by well-developed gluteal muscles. If all grade horses (let alone fully registered animals) were "odd looking" like this fellow, Americans in both domestic and international competition would more often be winners. I know that gaitedness in a bloodline scares away many riders, but such concerns are groundless. Over a din of objections and the snickers of those who have forgotten that the Andalusian was the first "dressage breed," I encourage them to try American

Saddlebreds, Tennessee Walking Horses and their crosses when they are conformed like this gelding.

Horse #4: This mare, though she probably has never taken a "gaited" step in her life, is not suitable for dressage or for any type of general purpose riding. There is such a thing as too long and fine a neck. This limit is reached when neck length is more than about 1½ times the length of a horse's back. This mare is at that limit. In addition, her head is too big for the length and refinement of her neck.

Her coupling is all right but the series of lumps on the croup reveal: (1) less-than-perfect bone structure with overlying muscular strain, (2) excessive development (hypertrophy) of muscles which erect the tail, and (3) hypertrophy of the upper part of the hamstring muscles, where they root on either side of the tail. This development is not balanced by development of the protractors as in Horse #1.

The mare is not as crooked ("angulated") in the hind limbs as Horse #3. Normally this would be good, but as a three-gaited mare, she will be required to produce the type of hock action typical of crooked hind limbs. To get that kind of motion, this mare will have to be ridden very hollow and disengaged. This is what her owner is probably doing, as indicated by the profile of the horse's topline, underline and the muscular developments already discussed.

This mare is a little weak-legged all around and "cut out" under the hocks. The grass does not hide the excessive length of her front feet. The developing dish visible on the left fore reveals the beginning of a mechanical rotation of the coffin bone that will eventually result either in the fetlock knuckling forward or in a clubbed foot.

THE NECK: LAB EXERCISE 3

Getting To The Root Of Ewe Neck

How the lower curve in the chain of vertebrae gives rise to an "upside-down" crest

Ewe-necked horses are usually defined as those possessing a "sunken" or "upside-down" crest, but the ewe-necked condition goes deeper than that, back to the bones. When the lower curve is deep and wide — no matter what the size and shape of the upper curve may be — the horse has the bone structure for ewe neck.

Depending upon the quality of a horse's training, his fitness and the skill and knowledge of his rider, a ewe neck can be minimized. Such horses do, however, have a special need for their riders to provide effective leg and seat aids. Because of the low, wide shape of their lower neck curve, in the early and middle stages of training, these horses must be ridden with the poll no higher than the withers in order to make the neck-telescoping gesture effective or even possible.

Here we present three examples of horses who possess the bone structure which results in the external appearance known as ewe neck. Since this characteristic is often hard to recognize, these examples are particularly helpful. The group includes one horse who lacks the bone structure for a ewe neck; see if you can tell which one it is.

Analysis

Horse #1: A more obvious example of the bone structure supporting a ewe neck could not be presented. The mare's shoulder is fairly upright and meaty, which could be forgiven if her neck didn't loop, vulturelike, forward and upward from it. Fortunately, the neck possesses an equally generous upper curve, which enhances the mare's "turnover" or "mitbah" and saves her from being hammer-headed as well as ewe-necked, a common combination.

It is probable that this mare is either ridden well or infrequently, for her neck shows no muscular bulges in excess of the minimum dictated by her bone structure. Although ewe-necked horses are often said to have their necks "set on high," this is not true of their bone structure. Instead, it is true of their head *carriage* when they are ridden, for they typically become "stargazers," poking their noses up and out and getting over or above the bit.

Horse #2: The woman who owns this gelding writes to say that he cast himself in a stall as a four-year-old and displaced a vertebra in his neck. As a result, the gelding carries his head cocked to the right and has lost some of the vision in his left eye. Despite the fact that this type of neck injury usually renders a

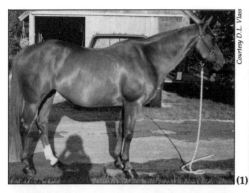

Courtesy M. Micklo

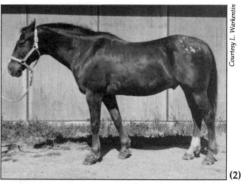

Courtesy L. Warkentin

Courtesy D.L. Vlass

Courtesy S. Fink

(1)

(2)

(3)

(4)

(1) **20-year-old Quarter Horse mare**
(2) **10-year-old Appaloosa gelding**
(3) **18-year-old Quarter Horse mare**
(4) **6-year-old Tennessee Walking Horse gelding**

horse dangerously uncoordinated, his owner reports that he is very sure-footed and is shown in English and Western pleasure, in sidesaddle and hunter classes and is trail ridden in the mountains. Recently, she has begun to school him in dressage.

In compensating for the neck injury, which is probably located at the junction between the skull and the first neck vertebra (the poll joint), the short extrinsic muscles of the poll (see Appendix A) have become overdeveloped, causing them to appear swollen. When these muscles are contracted, they act to lift the horse's nose. If the horse activates them during dressage, he will seem to be hard-mouthed or will pull against the reins.

The fact that this fellow is in the early stages of dressage training is indicated by the lack of muscular development in the lower triangle of the neck and by the fact that the tubelike complexus muscle, which extends back from his bulging mitbah, is prolonged only halfway to the shoulder. Although somewhat better in neck structure than Horse #1, the gelding is still ewe-necked, and his training needs are similar to

53

those of other horses with this conformation.

Horse #3: Though the muscular development of this mare's neck is strikingly different from that of Horse #2, the proportions of the S curves of their neck vertebrae are similar. Like Horse #1, both Horse #2 and this subject show a prolonged "dip" in front of the withers, a telltale sign of a wide and deep lower S curve.

The muscular development of this mare's neck is typical of ewe-necked horses ridden by riders with average skills: the short muscles of the mitbah and the brachiocephalicus are well-developed, and a strong rhomboideus, which adds a "false crest," is evident (see Appendix A). At the same time, the tubelike complexus is nowhere to be seen, and the lower triangle of the neck is hollow. This horse is a bit "hard-mouthed" and probably does not make the neck-telescoping gesture when ridden.

Some strain is likewise evident in the musculature of the mare's loin area. Her coupling, although well-structured by nature, is uneven in profile and appears somewhat "stretched." Neck structure and function tend to parallel and predispose loin structure and function.

Horse #4: This "fooler" is actually a straight-necked horse. He lacks the characteristic dip in front of the withers shown by the other three. His bone structure becomes clear when you compare his neck to the equally long but differently shaped neck of Horse #1.

This is a nice riding horse, with a back that is short, well-coupled, broad and strong. The quarters are spectacular: long from front to back (point of hip to point of buttock) and deep (from point of hip to stifle). The hocks are low, not because the gaskin is long, skinny and wobbly as is so often seen, but because the stifle joint lies lower than the horse's sheath. This simultaneously deepens the quarters and lowers the hock. The weakest aspect of this gelding is his front legs which, though substantial, show steep pasterns and overstraight knees.

The generally correct muscular development of this horse's neck is the product of the depth and strength of his underline. The fact that the circumference of the horse's torso from loin to groin is nearly equal to his heart girth enables him to carry himself athletically and almost guarantees correct neck carriage as a secondary result. Work over cavalletti and allowing the horse to stretch down and forward at the beginning and end of each session will put the finishing touches on an already good structure.

The Ideal Equine Neck

Why bone structure, not crestiness, is the critical factor from a functional point of view

In terms of shape and contribution to a horse's performance capability, the four necks presented here are the inverse of the ewe necks discussed previously. Although all of these horses' necks are well crested, crestiness is not the critical factor in creating these desirable shapes. Rather, as always it is the bone structure at the root of the horse's neck that forms the basis for a high arch.

In a ewe-necked individual, the upper curve of the S-shaped chain of neck vertebrae is short, while the lower curve is broad and deep. Measuring from side to side, the base of the lower curve is the neck's thickest point. (This point can be palpated in a live horse by pressing the palms of your hands against the sides of the neck.) While the widest point of a ewe neck lies lower than halfway down the shoulder bed, the thickest point of an arched neck, as illustrated by the horses presented here, is located relatively high. This is a reflection of the underlying bone structure; in an arched neck, the lower curve of the S is relatively shallow.

The desirability of an arched neck goes far beyond beauty. The shape and proportions of the chain of bones within make it easy for the horse to perform the neck-telescoping gesture. This important ability is powered by the contraction of the scalenus muscles, which connect the first rib to the neck (Figure 22). In a ewe-necked horse, these muscles are less likely to develop their leverage capacity. In a horse whose neck is arched, however, the potential for muscle development is great. Contraction of the scalenus muscles acts to raise and steady the root of the neck, to establish unity in movement between the neck and the torso, to stretch the topline and to cause the horse to go willingly and *thoroughly* onto the bit (Figure 25).

Each of the following horses is not only an excellent specimen of his or her breed, but also a useful, sturdy, sound and well-moving riding horse.

Analysis

Horse #1: This stallion is exceptionally well proportioned and possesses a beautiful head. Like most other structurally excellent horses, he is sound and therefore comfortable, unworried and trainable. His easy disposition is evidenced by the interested, but not intensely pricked attitude of his ears, and by the relaxation of the small muscles of his face, especially around the eye.

The stallion's neck is not only beautifully shaped and just the right length, but the crest carries back over his well-shaped withers, making it look as if the neck springs from the center of the back. This conformation increases the neck's leverage capabilities,

(1) 12-year-old Morgan stallion
(2) 6-year-old American Saddlebred mare
(3) 15-year-old Appaloosa gelding
(4) 11-year-old 7/8ths Arabian gelding

(1)

Courtesy A. Councill

(2)

Courtesy S. Cobb

(3)

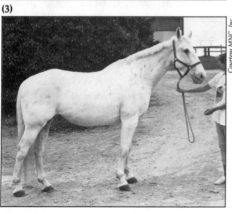

Courtesy MNC, Inc.

(4)

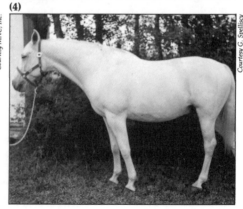

Courtesy G. Spelliscy

which maximize the effect of the neck-telescoping gesture upon the back.

This fellow's conformation is further enhanced by a topline that carries smoothly back over the loins; a coupling that is ideally placed, broad and short; well-sprung ribs; and sufficient length in both the croup and the pelvis.

Horse #2: The mare's neck is well shaped and "set on" her very laid-back shoulder as high as is possible. Her withers end more abruptly than Horse #1's and aren't positioned so far behind the shoulders. The conformation of this mare's shoulders, withers and crest is very similar to Horse #4's despite the difference in their poses.

The rest of the mare's topline is smooth, her coupling is short and strong, and the ribs carry well back in a torso that is exceptionally deep through the heart girth.

Horse #3: This gelding's "uphill" build stems from three main factors: his straight, open-angled (and therefore short) hind legs; his long forearms (compare Horse #2; contrast Horses #1 and #4); and the high placement of the root of his neck. Though his neck is not as cresty as the others', its thickest part is still placed exceptionally high. The topline flows from the poll down over very tall withers which end a bit abruptly but still well behind the shoulders.

The gelding's worst feature is his coupling, which is peaked and set back, lengthening the loins and shortening the croup. He also needs conditioning: ideally, the gluteal muscles on the top of the pelvis, the rectus abdominis of the belly and the complexus of the neck would be larger in a horse possessing such excellent bone structure (see Appendix A for muscle location). With conditioning, his groin will drop and his neck will acquire more crest.

Horse #4: This gelding's bone structure is also excellent, though at first glance he seems somewhat light of leg and unusually thick through the base of the neck. The explanation comes from his owner, who writes to confess that he's gotten "a bit chubby" since she has been unable to ride him regularly. The gelding is not only pudgy about the neck, but around the tailhead as well, which produces an undulating topline at his hind end. Incidentally, these can depict a type of hypothyroidism — a condition seen with low output of the hormone thyroxin from the horse's thyroid gland. A veterinary examination and hormone assay would indicate whether this is the case. If so, the remedy will depend on the condition's extent. Simply reducing the horse's grain ration while increasing his exercise may compensate for his condition if the effect is only slight. In more serious cases, however, thyroid hormone supplementation may be necessary.

Significantly, however, this fellow isn't showing a lot of excess poundage from the underline: as his trim tummy shows, despite too many groceries and not enough exercise, he continues to move well, continually utilizing his ring of muscles. This is also indicated by the vertical depth of his body from loin to groin (contrast Horse #3).

His head is well shaped, with a chiseled look and prominent bones. Again note the relaxed, self-possessed expression. Especially pleasing is the depth of the muzzle, which does not look as if it had gotten stuck in a pencil sharpener.

Chapter 3

How To Look At A Horse's Forequarter

Standing or in motion, it's what's up front that counts

In the history of horsemanship, more has been said about this part of a horse's anatomy than any other. The importance of the forequarter is in direct proportion to the degree to which the horse is required by its use to travel "on the forehand." It is important to neither misunderstand nor overinterpret this term.

At rest, the average horse carries 65% of his weight on the forelegs, so when the Romans named the horse *equus* — meaning the animal which carries itself in balance, with equal weight on all four legs — they stretched the point with regard to the standing animal.

In movement, however, their observations were correct, for when a well-conformed horse engages his hindquarters (i.e., flexes the lumbosacral joint), thus activating his ring of muscles in movement (Chapter 3, Volume I), he *does* carry his weight equally on all four legs. The horse is the only hoofed mammal which is naturally and effortlessly able to raise his whole forequarter by engaging his hindquarters, rounding (basculing) his back and making a neck-telescoping gesture. These are the three biomechanical components or cardinal signs, not only of "ring" function, but of collection.

59

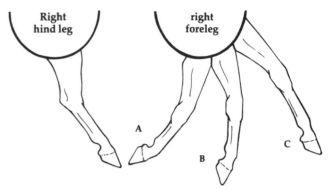

Figure 28. All gaits from trot to pace are merely points on a timing continuum. The fundamental difference between different gaits is not the pattern of hoofprints in the sand, but the timing relationship between front and hind feet. For any given hind limb position (left half-circle), an infinite number of corresponding right forelimb positions are possible. Three possible forelimb positions (right half-circle) are shown here. When the forelimb is in position A, the horse is trotting. When the forelimb is in an intermediate position (B), the horse is producing one of the ambling gaits, such as the rack, one of the paso gaits, or the running walk. When the forelimb is in the extended position (C), the horse is pacing.

While a horse cannot be said to be on the forehand at rest, he travels that way when in a state of zero collection — that is, when he makes no effort to flex the lumbosacral joint and thus produces no basculed back posture and no neck-telescoping gesture. Just as there are degrees of collection, depending on how strongly and thoroughly the horse's "ring" functions, so there are also degrees of traveling on the forehand.

The horse travels most on the forehand when his hindquarters are *dis*engaged (when he opens instead of closes his lumbosacral joint, thus permitting his stifles and hocks to trail behind). As a corollary to disengagement, the horse's back sags instead of arching up into a weight-bearing bascule. Likewise, instead of making a neck-telescoping gesture, the horse on the forehand raises his poll and appears ewe- or even elk-necked. Despite appearances, pulling the horse's head and neck up or back does *not* lighten his forehand. Instead, by preventing the horse from making a neck-telescoping gesture, basculing the back and engaging its hindquarters, pulling the horse's head and neck back actually forces him to carry more weight on his forequarters than while standing at rest (Figure 23a,c,e). Due to the horse's unique anatomy and functional design, the belief that live equines work like wooden rocking horses is entirely erroneous (see Volume I, page 36).

Speed, as well as ill-founded theory based on fashion, also forces horses to the forehand. This is because the efficiency required for high speed requires that the horse stiffen his neck and torso. This stiffening does not completely prevent engagement of the hindquarters, but it does prevent or inhibit bascule and the neck-telescoping gesture.

While flat, harness and endurance racing are all examples of motion that sacrifice torso flexibility in the interest of speed, it surprises many to find that gaited riding also falls into this category. Surprising because, from the rider's point of view, gaited riding is very smooth and gives the impression of a light, fluid gliding. However, to the degree that a horse's footfall timing approaches that of a pace, the stiffer the horse must hold its torso in order to produce that gait. All the ambling gaits lie on a footfall-timing continuum from those closer to a trot, such as the foxtrot, to those closer to a pace, such as the rack (Figure 28). The fact that ambling gaits tend to stiffen a horse's torso and neck has been recognized for a thousand years by trainers of Spanish Jennets and the Caribbean and American varieties of Paso, who emphasize neck-bending and turning exercises as an indispensable part of training as well as proper maintenance for the finished horse.

Besides observing the three cardinal signs that reveal whether a horse is using his "ring" when he moves, thus relieving his forehand of weight, there are two other simple ways of deciding whether a horse is traveling on the forehand.

The first way is simply to observe the degree to which a horse's fore-pastern angle changes as weight passes over a given forelimb as he performs under saddle. How far does the fetlock joint descend to the ground? Is this distance the same for both front legs? Compare this distance to the height of the fetlock and the angle of the pastern when the horse is halted. The horse whose front fetlocks descend least toward the ground *compared to their resting state* travels least on the forehand.

Notice that many horses appear to travel lighter while being circled in one direction than in the other. Likewise, a horse might be lighter at trot than at the canter. The heaviness while performing one gait or one direction indicates that to be the gait or direction in which the horse stiffens his torso.

The second method requires making a movie of the horse in action. Traveling on the forehand is not just a function of weight on the forelimb; it is also a function of time. Filming your horse from the side can tell you how much time the horse spends weighting each of his legs. The amount of time corresponds proportionally to the amount of weight.

The method is simple. First, clip out a strip of frames that document one complete stride. One complete stride, or cycle, is counted from the first contact of the right foreleg with the ground to the next contact of the same leg. For simplicity's sake, let's say that this cycle occupies 100 frames of film.

Next, count the number of frames in which the horse stands on one or both front legs, but on *neither* hind leg. This number ranges from about 80 (in the case of a weighted big lick 'Walker) to 15 (in the case of a stallion of the Spanish Riding School of Vienna executing piaffe). Measuring "on the forehand" as a variable of time rather than weight clarifies its physiological effect on the horse. Being on the forehand to the horse is analogous to climbing rope for us. It involves the overuse of the muscles of the pectoral girdle: the same muscles of your chest, armpits, shoulders and neck which you'd feel straining if you were climbing rope. At the same time, it underutilizes the muscles of the lower back, abdomen and hind limbs (Figure 29).

Do not mistake this discussion as a plea to discontinue racing or gaited riding but an invitation to understand these activities for what they actually are. It is time to stop kidding ourselves that the majority of our park, three-gaited and dressage horses are light on the forehand. They're not.

The final lab exercises in this book give a systematic and detailed set of criteria and methods to enable you to recognize excellent front legs. If you're engaged in racing, three- or five-gaited riding, park, saddle-seat equitation or endurance, you simply will not succeed with anything less than excellent front legs. The same warning applies obviously to those in three-day eventing, jumping and hunting.

Polo, cutting, reining and dressage mounts can

Figure 29. A, a weighted "big lick" Tennessee Walking Horse doing the running walk. The horse stands on one or both front legs in 75% of the frames and stands on front legs only in 25% of frames. By any measure, this horse is "on the forehand." Dressage horses at extended trot frequently do no better; a horse at trot should never be caught standing on only one front leg. B, a stiff-backed and high-headed dressage horse. Like the Walker above, he stands on one or both front legs 75% of the time. However, in four frames out of 12, this horse stands on no front legs; in frames 5 and 11 the horse momentarily achieves self-carraige, in which he propels himself forward by means of hind legs alone.

A

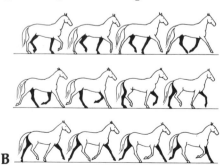

B

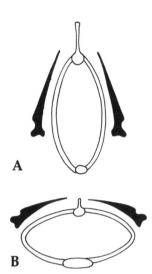

Figure 30. A, the horse's rib cage is elongated vertically and flattened from side to side; his shoulder blades work "against his sides." B, the human rib cage is elongated from side to side and flattened from front to back; our shoulder blades work "against our back."

get away with less structurally excellent front legs, because when well-executed, the horse works almost exclusively off his hocks. But a master horseman will tell you that he would rather not settle for anything but the best in forelimbs. For the rest of us mortals, who have to repeat movements or exercises or may have trouble obtaining collection because of our own lack of competence, excellent front legs are necessary insurance.

Now that we've concluded that all horses need excellent front legs, let's find out exactly what superb forequarters look like.

THE FOREQUARTER: LAB EXERCISE 1

The Right Angle On Shoulders

Upright or laid back, their position determines how the horse's forelimbs move

So far in this volume, we've thoroughly examined the structure and function of the equine topline. Now it's time to move downward to take a look at the bony elements of the forelimb, the uppermost of which is the shoulder blade, technically known as the scapula.

The horse's shoulder blades rest against his rib cage. Viewed from the front, the equine rib cage forms a more or less flattened oval shape, which is narrow from side to side. This is in marked contrast to the shape of the human rib cage, which is shallow from backbone to breastbone or back to front (Figure 30). As a result, a person's shoulder blades are positioned in a different manner than a horse's. If you bend forward at the waist so that your spine is horizontal like your horse's, you'll find that your shoulder blades lie horizontally, as if on a tabletop. By contrast, the horse's shoulder blades are set in a near-vertical position.

The orientation of each species' shoulder blades determines its basic capabilities for arm movement. People, like other primates, can grasp and hold things with their long, mobile arms and hands. We can easily swing from a branch. Horses obviously cannot. Their vertically oriented scapulas are designed for only one movement: gliding rotation in a fore-aft plane, a motion which can be compared to

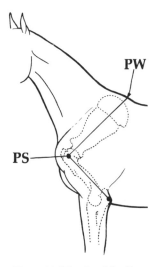

PW

PS

Figure 31. The shoulder line is measured from the point of withers (PW) to the point of shoulder (PS).

the path a soapy sponge follows when you wash a window.

The shoulder can rotate in every horse, yet in some individuals the shoulder blades rest at a steep angle. In others the angle is much more sloping, "low" or "laid back." You can estimate the angle of a horse's shoulder by finding the peak of his withers and the point of his shoulder. A line connecting these two points, when compared to the horizontal, defines the shoulder angle (Figure 31).

Many books on conformation indicate that the lower the shoulder angle, the better. Yet this generalization is inaccurate. Every structure has some desirable capabilities, but no structure is all good or bad. As always, in biomechanical study, everything is a trade-off.

The muscles that move the horse's scapula are rooted along the rear edge of the bone. When these muscles contract, they rotate the top of the shoulder blade down; this in turn pulls up the horse's knees (see Appendix A). Thus, an upright shoulder predisposes a horse for greater knee action (in a gaited or park horse context) and also to carry his knees well (in a hunter-jumper context). The flip side of an upright shoulder is that a horse so endowed may give an inelastic, rough-feeling ride; be less able to absorb forelimb concussion and thus exhibit diminished soundness; and possess a tendency to "stand under" or to be pigeon-breasted (have a prominent sternum).

At the other conformational extreme stands the horse with a low shoulder angle. Low shoulder angles were "invented" by breeders who wanted draft and carriage horses that could more easily and comfortably carry their work collars. Later, horsemen noticed that a laid-back shoulder is useful in other ways, but contrary to the information presented in many books, high knee action is not one of them. If a horse with a low shoulder angle has high action, he derives it either from training, the addition of artificial appliances, or through other forelimb components. As a hunter-jumper, such a horse can fold prettily but is not the one who can "put his hooves in his ears" to get his rider out of a tight spot going cross-country. As a dressage horse, he tends to have low, slightly round action carried out in front of the breast. When a Morgan Horse — a breed that frequently possesses a very low shoulder angle —

moves out at a road trot, he exhibits this weather-vane-like form in the extreme. The flip side of this attractive way of going is that horses with very low shoulder angles tend to first strike on the toe, slam the heel and frequently do not grow heel as fast as they grow toe.

As you examine the horses in this section's photos, check not only for shoulder angle but also for a shelf-like shoulder bed that defines where the neck enters the chest. A clean shoulder bed indicates correct muscular development at the root of the neck and on the shoulder blade, and is a sure sign of a mobile, free-swinging shoulder.

Analysis

(1) 17-year-old Thoroughbred gelding
(2) 5-year-old Arabian gelding
(3) 4-year-old Arabian-American Saddlebred gelding
(4) 12-year-old Thoroughbred gelding

Horse #1: This is an unusually low shoulder angle for a Thoroughbred horse. Notice that the farrier has maintained plenty of heel on this gelding, and that the angle of the fore hoof is steeper than that of the shoulder. This hoof trim contributes to maintaining correct alignment of the pastern bones, thereby reducing stress on the pastern, fetlock and knee joints. In hoof trimming, it is more important to mini-

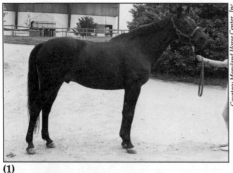

(1)

Courtesy Maryland Horse Center, Inc.

Courtesy L. Darnell

(2)

Courtesy M. Cordan

(3)

Courtesy the author

(4)

mize joint stress than it is to meet any arbitrary rule about shoulder angle.

An owner may, however, want to measure a horse's shoulder angle in order to assess performance capability. In this horse, the withers carry exceptionally well back into the free span of the back, and the shoulder blade is centered on the line connecting the withers to the point of the shoulder. This gelding is used as a dressage schooling horse and does very little jumping.

Horse #2: This horse shows a shoulder angle that is neither too steep nor too laid back. The clean, shelf-like shoulder bed implies a mobile shoulder, something that a hunter-jumper or three-day-event rider would be grateful for. So freely does this fellow's shoulder slide over his ribs that, even at five years of age, he often lies down with both forelegs stretched out parallel in front of him, like a dog (Figure 32). He can raise his knees high enough to "put his hooves in his ears", and when he gets bored with the view from his stall, he steps up to put both front feet on the stall door to peer out from on high. You may agree that this is a bit hard on the stable furniture, but it's a sign of athletic ability nonetheless.

This fellow is especially suitable for use as a show hunter and is an all-around excellent horse, despite minor shortcomings (his pelvis could be slightly longer; his coupling slightly farther forward; his bone slightly more substantial). However, as a wise breeder once said, "For every thousand people who can pick faults, you'll find hardly one who can pick a

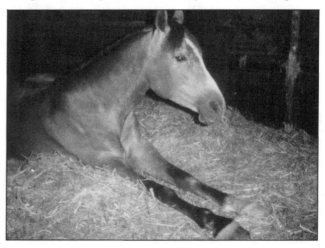

Figure 32. A five-year-old Arabian gelding lying down in his stall with legs extended to the front, like a dog. Such extreme shoulder flexibility is rare in horses and is an indicator of athletic prowess.

horse." This gelding scores high in the harmonious integration of his parts and in overall balance (compare him to Horse #3).

Horse #3: A long and shapely neck is this gelding's one outstanding conformation feature. His shoulder lies at about the same angle as that of Horse #2. However, compared with any of the others, his neck posture is poor — it's carried quite low at the root. Overall body balance is as important as shoulder angle in determining this.

Standing rump-high, this gelding has hind legs that are too long to match his front legs. The resulting downward slope of the topline will cause a plethora of difficulties, starting with saddling. Moderate withers prevent the saddle from actually sliding up onto the neck, but keeping the buttons of the fore arch from gouging the shoulders with every posting stroke will be a challenge. Since this gelding is underweight and out of condition, as well as narrow-backed with the coupling set fairly far back, his whole topline is in jeopardy under saddle. A graduated program of regular, physically challenging exercise as well as larger rations may help him.

This horse is balanced like a wheelbarrow. It's easy enough to make him move forward, but very difficult to get his front end up off the ground. Without expert training, this gelding will offer a suspensionless "stepping trot" and a four-beat canter. In changing from walk to trot or trot to canter, or if asked to jump something, he'll throw his head up and may even hit his rider in the face. Adding a tiedown device is no solution; it will just imprison him on the forehand.

This gelding's teenaged owner can help him most by enlisting a professional horseperson to advise her in feeding, conditioning and training. For any type of showing or athletic endeavor beyond hacking, this gelding's great physical limitations are likely to be beyond the owner's ability to remedy.

Horse #4: This horse has high, steep withers that peak far forward (compare them to those of Horse #1). His shoulder angle is remarkably steep, and as a result his neck extends more forward than upward. The shoulder bed is vague and meaty-looking, indicating restricted shoulder movement. What saves this gelding is his overall body balance — his topline, the opposite of Horse #3's, rises from back to front.

With powerful quarters, a nice deep chest and an upright shoulder angle — implying an ability to raise the knees — this gelding might be able to compete successfully as a jumper. However, he's light of bone all around, has small, round joints, and a grade-B coupling. Therefore, he's not likely to stay sound in that division. He's used in dressage, but paddles and has unfashionably high knee action. Moreover, he's a somewhat rough ride. His head and neck "rattle" and it is difficult for him to stay on the bit. With all their shortcomings, horses like #3 and #4 provide great learning experiences for their owners; horsemanship develops through working with teachers like these.

THE FOREQUARTER: LAB EXERCISE 2

The Lesser-Known Arm Bone

Its length and angle dictate the style of a horse's front-end movement

The previous exercise served as an introduction to the whole of the horse's foreleg, because the higher in a limb a bone is located, the greater its overall influence on the swing of that limb. Moving down the foreleg, the bone below the shoulder blade (scapula) is the humerus, or arm bone.

Although the length and resting angle of the humerus are of great importance in determining how a horse moves in front, this bone is often overlooked by all but the most astute judges of equine conformation. Perhaps neglect of the humerus (and of the femur, the equivalent bone of the hind limb) is due to the fact that in horses these bones are bound up in flesh and are therefore difficult to visualize clearly. Once you know where to look, however, the humerus is easy to find; it connects the point of the shoulder to the elbow.

Of all the joints in the horse's forelimb, only the broad ball-and-socket joint located between the scapula and the humerus is capable of side-to-side movement. This allows the humerus to swing not only from back to front, thus raising or lowering the elbow, but also allows the front limbs to cross each other for lateral movements.

While the shoulder blade governs the entire fore-limb, the humerus determines the way in which an individual horse folds and unfolds the elbow, knee and fetlock joints. Whether long and steep, long and horizontal, short and steep or short and horizontal, the humerus determines the style of a horse's front-end movement in the following ways:

• **The longer the humerus, the more "scopey" the horse's gait** since swinging a long humerus results in a greater arc, or scope, at the elbow end of the bone. Scope is defined as the ability to move the elbow away from the torso, either toward the front, as in a jumper clearing a spread fence, or to the side, as in a dressage horse executing a fluid traversale. Scope enables a cutting horse to crouch in front, spreading or crossing his forelegs as necessary to head the calf. Scope is a very desirable characteristic. It has saved the neck of many a fox hunter, trail rider and three-day eventer, enabling their horses to recover from a mistake after committing to an obstacle, whether it be a log, a slide or a Normandy bank.

• **The shorter the humerus, the more choppy the horse's gaits will be**. A horse with a short humerus moves with correspondingly short, stiff strides, has difficulty with lateral work and is frequently dangerous to jump. Choppy-gaited is the opposite of scopey.

• **The steeper the resting angle of the humerus, the higher the horse can raise his knees**. This is of obvious importance in choosing a three-gaited, fine harness or park horse, especially when the owner adheres to a policy of natural trimming and shoeing and eschews appliances in training and showing. The most spectacular natural action is possessed by horses with the following combination of characteristics: a moderately upright shoulder angle (near 60 degrees); a long, steep humerus; and moderately long cannon bones with high knees.

The same combination of factors produces the hunter-jumper who not only folds nicely but can virtually "put his hooves in his ears" in negotiating a grand-prix course. The only difference between the successful jumper and the three-gaited horse is that the jumper needs to have short cannon bones, low knees and substantial bone to preserve soundness through repeated landings.

• **The more horizontal the resting angle of the**

humerus, the less natural ability a horse will have for high action or tight folding. A horizontally oriented humerus guarantees that the horse will be a "grass clipper" — when asked to jump, he will have difficulty raising his forearms to level and may hang his knees.

In scanning the examples, first locate the horse's humerus. Then compare its length to that of the scapula. To be considered long, the humerus must be at least 50 percent as long as the shoulder blade. Then look at the resting angle of the humerus. Ideally, the angle between the line of the humerus and the line of the shoulder will be wider than 90 degrees. In which of these examples is this not the case?

Analysis

Horse #1: This mare is especially useful in illustrating the principles under scrutiny in this lab exercise because she is one of those Thoroughbreds who simply doesn't pack a lot of body fat. As a result, nearly every muscle in her body is visible and this, in turn, makes the location of the bones easy to see. The humerus, demarcated by the dotted line on Figure 33, is short; it only covers half the length of her shoulder. The angle between the shoulder and arm at the point of shoulder is just acceptable at 90 degrees.

The muscles of the mare's neck are thin along the upper side but thick along the lower side; the lower triangle of the neck is hollow. The desirable complexus muscle is not at all evident. The incorrect muscling of her neck and the rather thick, stiff-looking muscling of her shoulder and arm have developed together. These are the signs of a horse that travels on the forehand.

The structure of her back, loins, croup, hindquarters, gaskins and hocks leaves me wondering why she travels so badly, because she has excellent structure everywhere behind the withers. Her front legs are also OK, although I don't like the over-straight knees. Perhaps her lack of self-carriage is due merely to youth and light use. Her short humerus and close shoulder angle indicate that she does not have spectacular scope, but she is nevertheless well worth someone's time to teach her to go correctly onto the bit in self-carriage.

Horse #2: Like almost all other members of his

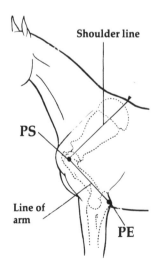

Figure 33. The line of the arm is measured from the point of shoulder (PS) to the point of elbow (PE). The shoulder angle is formed by the shoulder line and the line of the arm joining at the point of shoulder.

breed, this American Saddlebred gelding shows a very long, steep humerus that forms a wide-open angle with the shoulder blade at the point of shoulder. This conformation guarantees that the horse will be scopey and free-moving. I'm also pleased to see such a good hindquarter on a Saddlebred. The shadow on this photograph draws a perfect picture of the horse's pelvis. The shadow stretches from point of hip in front, dips as it crosses the prominence of the horse's hip socket and ends just at the point of buttock. Farther down, he shows well-structured hocks and correct angulation of the hind legs.

The weakest part of his construction is his loins. He shows a medium-length back that is imperfectly coupled and obviously undermuscled. The circumference from loin to groin is small. His owner writes to say that he's "not being starved...you just have to understand, this is a big strong three-year-old, so they are working him hard and not graining him." No, he is not yet at the point of starvation (I don't see

(1) 4-year-old Thoroughbred mare
(2) 3-year-old American Saddlebred gelding
(3) 3-year-old Morgan-Arabian gelding
(4) 26-year-old Appaloosa gelding

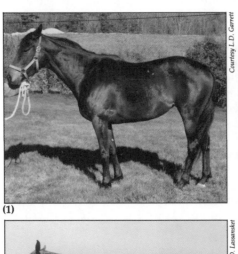

(1)

Courtesy L.D. Garrett

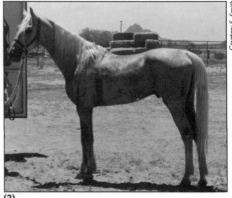

(2)

Courtesy S. Smith

(3)

Courtesy D. Lassamsket

(4)

Courtesy C. Reeves

ribs), but witholding feed is the wrong way to go about curing this horse's resistances, which stem not from excess strength but a deficit of it, just where it counts most — in his back and belly. He needs grain to build muscles, and he needs a trainer who understands how to use cavalletti, ground driving and stretching the neck down and forward to build the back and belly strength this horse desperately needs.

Horse #3: This gelding shows a neck construction that is in striking contrast to Horse #2, while the structure of his shoulder and arm are exactly the same (compare lengths and angles of both the shoulder blade and the humerus in each). Like Horse #2, the angle at the point of this horse's shoulder is much wider open than 90 degrees. This gelding should be just as pretty and scopey in front as the Saddlebred even though his neck is much shorter.

This gelding's back also contrasts sharply with that of Horse #2. The bone structure of the loin coupling is about the same, as is the total length of the back, but this horse shows much fuller musculature on top and a greater loin-to-groin circumference.

Horse #4: This gelding shows a fault common in stock-type horses: a near-horizontal humerus. The horozontal orientation of this gelding's arm is the result of selection for a long shoulder line, which is a desirable characteristic until the point of shoulder drops too low, as it has in this individual. A shoulder this long and steep would be workable if the angle between it and the arm were maintained at 90 degrees or wider — but as you can see, the angle is less than 90 degrees. As a result, this gelding is more markedly pigeon-breasted than any of the others. His arm construction deprives him of folding ability (he'll hang his knees over jumps) as well as the ability to crouch (as for cutting).

THE FOREQUARTER: LAB EXERCISE 3

Foundation Of The Forelimbs

How the upper arm bones influence the orientation of the lower front legs

Let's now look at the humerus from another angle, for this bone also relates to the structure of the horse's breast and is important in determining the

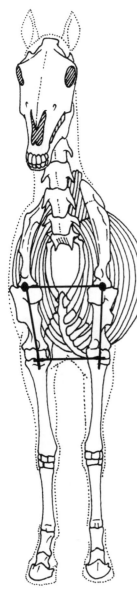

Figure 34. The "breast box" is visualized from the front and is composed of the left and right points of shoulder (above), and the left and right elbows (below). To locate the elbows, the analyst must "see through" the horse's forearms.

orientation of the front legs. In other words, the crookedness that plagues the equine forelimbs often begins with the structure of the breast.

Seen from the side, the humerus forms a sloping line which connects the point of the shoulder to the point of the elbow. If we move around to the front of the horse, we find that the humerus forms a line that slopes inward from the point of the shoulder (Figure 34). Depending on the amount of inward slope, the elbow may rest close to the rib cage (tight elbows) or farther from it (loose elbows).

To understand how having tight or loose elbows influences the orientation of the lower part of the legs, try mimicking the horse's forelimbs. First, turn your palms down. Then straighten your wrists so that your middle finger is in alignment with your forearm. Now stretch your arms out to the front. This gives you a technically "perfect" set of front legs below the breast. Now, without bending your wrists or fingers, clamp your elbows to your sides. What happens to the orientation of your "hooves"? Do you "toe out" or "toe in"? Now try the opposite movement, turning your elbows out like a bulldog's. Do you toe out or in? The lesson here is that a horse can have perfect front legs below the breast, but if his elbows are too tight he'll toe out; if they're too loose, he'll toe in. It is the "set" of the humerus at the point of the shoulder that determines the orientation of the elbow and of the lower part of the forelimb.

Before reading the analysis, locate the following in each of the four examples:

- the left and right points of the shoulder (marked by dots)
- the left and right elbows (marked by plus signs).

On each horse, form a box by connecting the two points of the shoulder and the two points representing the elbows. A square box is the foundation for a good set of front legs. A box that's wider at the bottom indicates that the horse will toe in. A box that's markedly narrower at the bottom indicates that the horse will toe out, and will plait or "walk the line" when moving. While this conformation is a fault, an asymmetrical box is even worse. If the box leans to the right or left, the horse may not have been "squared up" when photographed. More ominously, he may not be weighting his feet equally due to foot pain, or he may have a curving spine. A box that has a markedly sloping top or bottom reveals that one of the horse's legs is shorter than the other one.

Analysis

Horse #1: This gelding has a very good set of front legs, but because his front hooves weren't quite even or squared up when photographed, he presents a not-quite-square "breast box." The left elbow is drawn up and back, which slightly compresses the left side of the box. This serves to illustrate the importance of squaring the horse before jumping to any conclusions about the animal having foot pain, a curved spine or a short foreleg.

This gelding shows slightly loose elbows, and as a result he toes in slightly when he moves. His square breast box also exemplifies the ideal. Notice how his forelimbs seem to come right off the edges of his chest, which is also of ideal width. Notice, too, how flat his pectoral muscles are; he does not overuse them because he travels in self-carriage.

This gelding is of interest because of his base-narrow stance, which also derives from his loose-elbow construction. Carrying this construction to an extreme (as shown in the next lab exercise) produces undesirable "bulldog" construction. This fellow is, however, a great old horse, still sound and in active

(1) 24-year-old Quarter Horse gelding
(2) 8-year-old Welsh-cross mare
(3) 6-year-old Quarter Horse mare
(4) 10-year-old Quarter Horse gelding

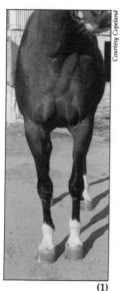
(1)

Courtesy Copeland

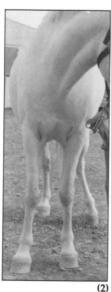
(2)

Courtesy E. Natrelis

(3)

(4)

Courtesy Maryland Horse Center, Inc.

service at the age of 24. His one forelimb flaw is a rotation of the right cannon bone under its knee (see Lab Exercise 5). The gelding toes out on the right not because he has a tight right elbow, but solely because of this rotation.

Horse #2: This mare's chest appears very narrow because she has very tight elbows, each of which is drawn so close to the chest that the elbows actually lie under it. The tightness of a horse's elbows begins with his bone structure but is maintained by stiffness and tension in the pectoral muscles which span the gap between the horse's breastbone and humerus (see Appendix B).

Because its origin lies in the bone structure, this conformation, to a certain extent, has to be accepted in horses as inborn. However, tight elbows can be improved through loosening and stretching of the pectoral muscles (see "The Gift Of Lightness"). Horses develop tight, hard, short pectoral muscles when they habitually travel on the forehand. When a mare spends her life dragging herself forward by means of her front legs, her pectoral muscles become short, stiff and overdeveloped and pull the arm bones in against the body. This effort stabilizes the forelimb but also causes the horse to travel narrow in front and the hooves to toe out, as here.

This habit can be changed by altering the horse's overall state of balance to one of self-carriage, in which the hind limbs do at least half the locomotory work. Many horses benefit from having their pectoral muscles "strummed" through manual massage or the therapeutic touch (T.E.A.M.®work) developed by Linda Tellington-Jones. Applied to this horse, these therapies would likely result in a wider-appearing chest, more distance between the knees and straighter-pointing toes. The outward deviations shown by both fore cannons here, however, will be unaffected by these therapies.

Horse #3: This mare has an excellent, wide-open breast box, similar to Horse #1's, although her chest is a tad wider. At the same time, she shows less tendency for base-narrowness. Used hard for stock penning and cutting, this mare is the kind of athlete which Quarter Horse breeders have always striven to produce. Her one forelimb flaw is the offset of the right cannon bone under its knee. Offset or "bench" knees cause twisting and stress in the joint every time weight passes over it. Bench knees also predispose to the development of splints. This mare is definitely of breeding quality, but I would look for a stallion with perfect front legs before arranging a mating.

Her feet also need attention: they're trimmed too short and appear "puddled" or "pancake-footed," with the angles of the walls not steep enough. This is not the natural conformation of her hooves; it was caused by trimming her feet too short in her first two years of life. Unfortunately, once established, this foot conformation is very difficult to change.

Horse #4: This horse has a number of torso and limb asymmetries, and it's no accident that he's hard to square up. Notice that both of his front hooves face to the right; at the same time, his left elbow is held farther away from the rib cage than the right one. The breast box is very asymmetrical. An inspection of the horse's back from above reveals a right lateral curvature of the spine. Notice also the uneven development of the pectoral musculature. A big, useful-looking gelding, this fellow competes in low-level eventing but has been known to stop or run out unexpectedly. In light of his "lopsided" bone structure, I'd say the behavior probably has its roots in physical discomfort.

THE FOREQUARTER: LAB EXERCISE 4

When Arms Are Asymmetrical

How every bone and joint of the forelimb affects a horse's stance

There's more to analyzing a horse's front legs than noticing whether his hooves point in or out. Few horses have hooves that point straight forward, either at a standstill or in motion, yet most horses function adequately or better. The reason for this discrepancy is that a horse is a live, three-dimensional, flexible being — not a diagram.

By drawing a picture of the "perfect" forelimb, we necessarily simplify what is naturally more complex.

The horse's *flat* shoulder blade (scapula), which is the uppermost part of his forelimb, must slide over the *rounded* rib cage, resulting in a peculiar outward oscillation. The humerus is oriented and articulated to the scapula in a way that dampens this oscillation effect. This is why, even in horses with "loose" elbows and deep armpits, the humerus still slopes somewhat inward when viewed from the front. With each stride, the humerus moves up and down, in and out, in countercoordination with the movements of both the shoulder blade and the forearm. Should the humerus actually descend straight down or even slope to the outside, abnormal movement, limb damage and unattractive conformation are the result.

The previous exercise discussed how the orientation of the humerus and the relative looseness or tightness of the elbow govern the set of the entire lower forelimb, making it possible for a horse to have perfect limb construction below the breast yet still toe in or out. In these examples, note the location of the points of the shoulder. Do they rest at the same height? Then check the inward slope of the upper arms. Are they the same on both sides of the body? Finally, consider the limbs below the breast. Why does each horse toe out, in or straight forward? The answer usually involves every one of the horse's forelimb bones and joints — not just the hooves.

Analysis

Horse #1: This filly shows markedly asymmetrical development of the shoulder blades and upper arm bones and, as a result, crooked front legs and abnormal hooves.

In the right forelimb, the shoulder blade lies as it should against the body wall, but the upper arm descends straight downward. Thus, the elbow is excessively loose, turning out like a bulldog's. Nature intended for this broad-chested, heavy filly to stand base narrow (with her hooves closer together than her shoulders) and to toe out slightly.

Her right forearm slopes inward as expected for this type of conformation. However, to compensate for the vertically oriented humerus, the cannon bone has twisted under the knee in the course of this filly's development, so that while the forearm and knee face nearly straight forward, the cannon bone is rotated nearly 30 degrees outward.

At the fetlock joint, the pastern bones are twisted inward about 15 degrees, while the hoof toes outward about 15 degrees — exactly the amount that would have been predicted for this filly had her right humerus developed along a normal orientation.

The fact that this developmental compensation isn't perfect, however, is shown by the dished hoof. This hoof profile indicates that with each stride, the filly's foot lands first on the outside wall, then on the inside wall. This lopsided footfall can be attributed directly to her steep humerus, which forces the forelimb to describe a wide, outward arc with each stride — a kind of paddling that originates at the shoulder joint and for which the bones and joints below cannot completely compensate.

In the left forelimb, the lower end of the shoulder blade lies far away from the body wall, and the point of the shoulder is much higher than on the right. For these reasons, the angle of this shoulder (as viewed from the side) is much less than that of the right side. While both elbows lie at the same height, the high placement of the left point of shoulder indicates that the left humerus is longer than the right one. Thus, the filly's left foreleg is longer than her right foreleg above the breast.

A chain of compensations for this asymmetry is

(1) Yearling Belgian filly
(2) 10-year-old Appaloosa mare
(3) 6-year-old Arabian gelding

Courtesy A. Gonzales

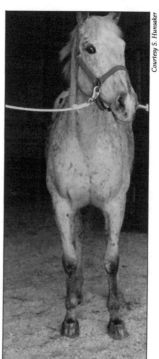

Courtesy S. Hunsaker

Courtesy the author

(2)

(3)

evident below the breast on the left side. The elbow is held tighter to the rib cage than normal, and as a result, the left forearm faces 30 degrees to the outside. The knee and cannon bone, however, face nearly straight forward, while the left pastern and hoof are actually twisted 15 degrees to the inside. This limb also paddles when the horse moves, but in this case the abnormal swing originates at the knee joint.

Asymmetrical limb length or development is not uncommon in horses. In fact, it is rare to find two front limbs which are exactly alike in any horse. In most cases, the left-to-right differences are minor and have little or no functional impact. This filly was helped by therapeutic shoeing, though the severity of her asymmetries, and the late date at which therapy was begun, will keep her from ever achieving her full athletic potential.

Horse #2: This mare also shows asymmetrical upper arm bones, but the problem here is merely one of orientation. Both her elbows and the points of her shoulders lie level, making her shoulder angles equal and her upper arm bones of comparable length. She toes out on both sides, but more noticeably so on the left. This is because her left humerus slopes inward more than her right one. Her left elbow also lies closer to the rib cage than does the right. Because the elbow is clamped in, the toe points out. There is no significant rotation of either cannon bone below the knees nor of the pasterns below the fetlock joints. The toes of the hooves line up with the front faces of the forearms, cannons and pasterns.

A subtle deviation of the left cannon bone (it tips slightly to the outside below the knee) is this mare's slight compensation for her tight elbow. In fact, her forelimb construction is nearly ideal below the breast. Corrective (actually cosmetic) shoeing or trimming in order to make this mare's *hooves* face straight forward would only harm her *joints*. The objectives of trimming and shoeing are to minimize stress on the limbs, not to make the limb match a graphic or diagrammatic ideal. The mare's well-shaped feet indicate normal breakover, and her joints show no evidence of stress or damage of any kind from the way she now moves.

Horse #3: This mare's front legs are not only normal and symmetrical from left to right, but nearly perfect in construction. The observer gets a slight impression of pigeon toes, even though the grass actually hides her hooves. A straight line cannot quite be dropped from either point of shoulder downward to bisect the limb, because both of this horse's cannon bones are slightly offset to the outside of the knee. However, the mare's big, shield-shaped knees help to compensate for the slightly offset cannons.

Even more indicative of normal functioning is the absence of either splints (bony enlargements often present on the outside of the cannon bone in horses with offset knees) or puffiness in any of the joints. As a result of her strong construction and ability to accomplish her work in a pain-free manner, this mare shows the eye typical of well-conformed horses — large, confident and relaxed.

THE FOREQUARTER: LAB EXERCISE 5

See How They Stand

Charting the factors that influence front-leg alignment

Major support elements of the forequarter lying below the the scapula and the humerus include the forearm (radius-ulna), the knee (carpus), the cannon bone, the long and short pasterns and the coffin bone. Misalignments at any of the joints between these support elements also contribute to forelimb crookedness. Toes that point out or in are not a cause but rather the *result* of the structure and alignment of all the other forelimb bones.

The chart (Figure 35) that accompanies this exercise will help you analyze your horse's forelimbs in front view. After reading the commentary for each of the following three examples, you'll be ready to grab a pencil and a clipboard and head for the stable to practice on your own horse — the most valuable teacher of all.

The first thing to keep in mind is that you will never see two front legs that are exactly alike — not even on the same horse. Therefore, it is necessary to analyze one leg at a time. The second thing to keep in mind is that you will rarely find a perfect equine leg.

There are very few limbs in which the proper front surface of the forearm, knee, cannon bone, fetlock joint, pasterns and the hoof *all* point forward. As

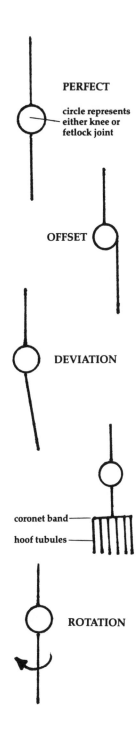

PERFECT

circle represents either knee or fetlock joint

OFFSET

DEVIATION

coronet band

hoof tubules

ROTATION

Figure 38. Charting The Horse's Forelimbs

feature/joint	left forelimb	right forelimb
knee joint: high rotations		
attachment of cannon bone to knee: rotations deviations offsets		
attachment of pasterns to cannons at fetlock joint: rotations deviations offsets		
relationship of hoof tubules and coronary band to pasterns: deviations		

a result, it's best not to stand squarely in front of the crease in the horse's breast when analyzing a limb. If you've decided to begin by analyzing the horse's left foreleg, for example, first walk around the left side of the horse until you're lined up with the front of the *knee*.

It's easy to walk around to the side if you're working with a live horse, but in a photo the point of view is fixed. Nevertheless, compare the left and right knees of Horse #1. The arrows help to indicate the knee orientation, which is nearly straight forward on the right, but points outward on the left some 15 to 20 degrees. This indicates that the horse holds his left elbow tighter against his body than his right elbow, and this, in turn, indicates either that the horse isn't standing "square" and needs to be repositioned, or that he is habitually bent or "crooked" to the left (such is the case, to some degree, with nearly all ridden horses, including this one).

Now that you're in a position to accurately analyze the left forelimb, let's complete the chart for that leg. First, in the box next to "knee joint: high rotations," record that you had to walk 15 degrees around to the left to line up your eyes with the front surface of the knee. Having done that, three areas of this leg remain to be examined: the attachment of the cannon bone under the knee, the attachment of the pasterns to the cannon bone at the fetlock joint and

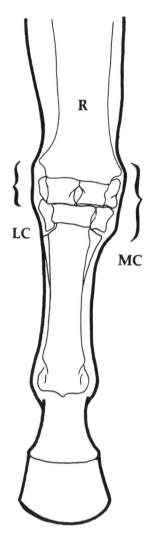

Figure 36. A lateral deviation of the cannon bone at the knee is frequently due to unequal development of the bones comprising the medial and lateral parts of the horse's carpus (knee). Here the bottom of the radius bone (R) and the medial carpal bones (MC) have undergone more growth than those on the lateral side (LC).

the relationship of the hoof tubules and coronary band to the pastern bones.

Misalignment of the limb bones in any of these three areas is classified as a **rotation**, a **deviation** or an **offset**. Refer to Figure 35 for a pictorial definition of these misalignments.

Analysis

Horse #1: Making use of our method, we saw that this gelding's left knee and forearm rotate outward 15 degrees. Additionally, the cannon bone rotates inward 10 degrees. There are no offsets, deviations or rotations at the fetlock joint, although there is a slight outside (lateral) deviation of the hoof tubules at the coronary band. As a result of these spiraling twists of the forelimb bones, the horse toes out about five degrees.

Now take a look at the gelding's right forelimb. From the elbow down, the leg rotates outward about five degrees. There are no other rotations, offsets or deviations. As a result of the nearly ideal carriage of the elbow, the lower part of the limb is nearly perfect — and so, too, are the hoof tubules, the breakover pattern of the foot, and the movement of the limb.

In the box next to "other comments" on the chart, there is room to include comments about pathologies (no physical ailments are present in this case) and blemishes (none). Also note the ideally large, shield-shaped knees, the substantial amount of bone and the general cleanness and lack of puffiness at all visible joints. Though minor flaws are evident (as they always are under intense scrutiny), this field hunter and cross-country horse has excellent legs with few peers among domestic horses.

Horse #2: This crossbred gelding also has excellent front legs and has been a comfortable, reliable and durable school horse for most of his long life. Examining his left foreleg reveals that his knee rotates outward five degrees. The cannon bone rotates inward slightly and is deviated five degrees to the outside as well. The pasterns deviate slightly to the outside while the hoof tubules deviate slightly to the inside. "Other comments" include slightly puffy fetlock joints, exceptionally substantial bone and heavy but rather short pasterns. On the right foreleg, the knee faces straight forward. The cannon bone rotates outward slightly and deviates five degrees to the outside. The pasterns and hoof tubules are straight. Other comments are the same as those noted for the left foreleg, with the addition of some thickening just above the coronary band on the right fore. (This may be investigated by palpation and perhaps X-rays.)

Horse #3: At the top, this mare starts with an excellent breast box and the desirable loose elbows, so that her forearms appear to come right off the sides of her chest. Tracing the line of her forearms downwards, one expects to see absolutely straight legs, but an interruption appears just below the knee joint of both front legs. Here the cannon bones are markedly offset to the outside. This conformation, called "bench knees," causes stress to the knee each time weight is applied to the leg. Since the lower end of the forearm does not line up with the upper end of the cannon bone, vertical shear occurs in the knee. This stresses the knee, and, through the course of development, tends to deform it and to encourage splint formation below it. In this mare, the deformation is most evident in the right knee.

(1) 18-year-old Thoroughbred gelding
(2) 20-year-old Thoroughbred-Tennessee Walking Horse gelding
(3) 10-year-old Thoroughbred mare

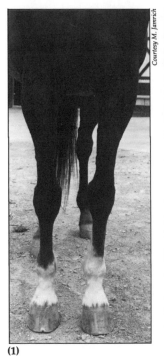

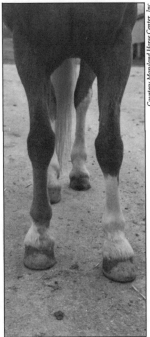

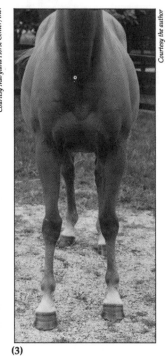

Courtesy M. Jamrich

Courtesy Maryland Horse Center, Inc.

Courtesy the author

(1) (2) (3)

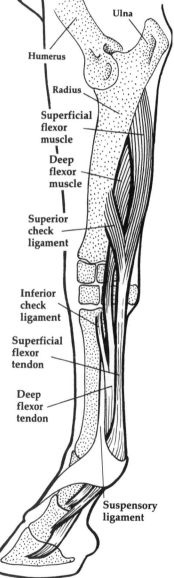

Figure 37. What horsemen call "the tendons" are continuations of the flexor muscles, which lie above the carpus. The flexor muscles (above the knee) must be properly conditioned to prevent injury to the flexor tendons (below the knee).

Ulna

Humerus

Radius

Superficial flexor muscle

Deep flexor muscle

Superior check ligament

Inferior check ligament

Superficial flexor tendon

Deep flexor tendon

Suspensory ligament

Putting The Knee In Perspective

Viewed from the side, the joint's contours provide telling clues about a horse's potential soundness

If you've practiced analyzing your horse's forelegs by using the chart in the last lab exercise (Figure 35), your eye for their structure, as viewed from the front, is likely to be much sharper. Now it's time to walk around to your horse's side in order to view his front legs from that equally important perspective.

The alignment of the bones and the size and quality of the joints are the first things to observe, just as you did when you viewed the horse from the front. A small "knee" joint (actually the carpus, which is equivalent to the human wrist) that's puffy in front or rounded in back is cause for concern. So is misalignment of the knee with the cannon or with the pastern bones. Ideally, there will be no lumps or sharp angles at the coronary band, the hoof tubules will extend perpendicular from the coronary band and the heel will be slightly more upright than the toe.

Next, examine the muscles originating on or passing over the forearm, as well as their tendons, which extend downward in front of and behind the knee joint. Ideally, the contractile or "fleshy" parts of these muscles, found above the knee, are smooth, sinewy and large without being disproportionate. Be aware, however, that extra fibrous components make these muscles feel harder and tougher than those of the horse's neck and quarters.

The noncontracting, tendinous parts of the flexor muscles, which horsemen simply call "the tendons," lie parallel to the back of the cannon and against the pastern bones (Figure 37).

Good tendons are prominent by virtue of their definition from surrounding tissues and not by size alone. They are easily distinguishable from the suspensory ligament and set well back from the splint bones and cannon bone. Good tendons are hard and tough, yet elastic; when the horse is standing, they feel neither like cement nor like modeling clay but rather like tightly stretched rope. Desirable tendons are not "tied in": the front and back profiles of the

Figure 38. The bones of the horse's forelimb can be aligned in a range of different ways. A, "calf knee," in which the axis of the radius is too vertical. As a result, the carpus and cannon bone tip backward, and the projection of the axis of the radius falls behind the hoof. B, a calf-kneed horse that is also "tied in" below the knee (arrows). This is the worst possible conformation for this body zone. C, "overstraight" knees. The axis of the radius is perfectly vertical. Since the radius is a curving bone, its lower end does not align perfectly with the top of the carpus and cannon bone. The projection of the radial axis falls slightly behind the hoof. D, perfect alignment. The axis of the radius slopes slightly to the front, thus ensuring perfect alignment of the curving radius with the carpus. The projection of the radial axis lies below the hoof but behind the navicular bone; it is directly below the bottom of the cannon bone. E, "buck knees," in which the radial axis tips too much toward the front. The projection of the radial axis falls too far forward; it lies in front of the bottom of the cannon bone, and directly beneath the navicular bone.

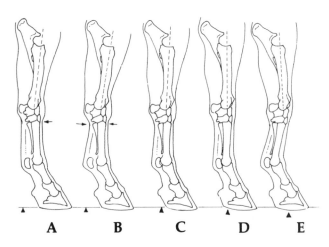

A   B   C   D   E

cannon are parallel and the circumference of the fore-limb, taken with a tape measure just below the knee, is equal to the circumference just above the fetlock.

The position and orientation of the forearm bone (the radius-ulna) are also important because the way this bone meets the top of the knee determines whether the horse will have straight forelegs, over-straight forelegs, calf knees or bucked knees (Figure 38).

Analysis

Horse #1: This very attractive mare serves as an example of a horse with straight forelegs. The muscles and tendons have the look (and feel) of excellent quality. Note the diameter of the widest part of the forearm. The fleshy flexor and extensor muscles are large and smooth, yet proportioned to match the bulk of the breast and shoulder. The three major muscles on the outside of the forearm are clearly defined.

As Figure 38 shows, the bone structure inside a straight foreleg isn't actually straight. Rather, the ideal foreleg, as exemplified by this mare, is ever so slightly bucked. Such a configuration helps to produce a shield-shaped knee with well-defined corners; its front profile is nearly (but not quite) flat.

Because of the excellent alignment of this mare's forearm bone and knee, she is the only horse in this

Courtesy the author *Courtesy K. Smith* *Courtesy P. Millott* *Courtesy the author*

(1) (2) (3) (4)

(1) 6-year-old Thoroughbred mare
(2) 4-year-old Anglo-Arabian gelding
(3) 2-year-old Bureau of Land Management feral horse from Oregon
(4) 8-year-old Thoroughbred gelding

group showing no puffiness either at the knee joint or over the tendons, despite having been raced as a two-year-old. The major structural weakness in this mare's forelimbs lies at the fetlock joint: her pasterns are thin and slightly too sloping, and her racing career has predictably produced a pair of puffy ankles which possibly point to osselets.

Horse #2: The overall structure of this very smooth gelding predisposes him to natural self-carriage. His owner intends to maintain his suppleness with dressage exercises while competing him as an endurance horse. Since endurance work tends to make horses stiff-backed, and because posture governs gait quality, stiff-backed endurance horses often become lame. For this horse, then, the endurance/dressage combination is a particularly good idea because his front legs — classic examples of the over-straight type (Figure 38) — are his weakest point.

Although this type of front leg is favored by many American judges, it is actually halfway between the ideal form and the seriously weak calf knee. Several drawbacks of overstraightness are visible in this photograph:

• The muscling on the forearm is thin compared to the muscling on the forearm of Horse #1.

• The knee joints are large but puffy-looking; note how they hang over in front.

• The left hoof has been allowed to get slightly too low in the heel, and as a result, the left foreleg is functionally calf-kneed. Low heels and upright pasterns interact with overstraight structure to increase backward strain on the knee joints.

• The tendons are well-defined but slightly tied in below the knee, diverging from the cannon toward the fetlock. The more calf-kneed the horse, the greater this divergence will be (compare this horse's conformation to Horse #1 and Horse #3).

Luckily, this gelding has excellent pasterns in terms of both length and angle, and first-class hooves in terms of size and probably of horn quality. If his owner keeps his hooves trimmed to the angle shown in the right foreleg, and works him between rides as well as in the off-season to stretch and supple his neck and torso, this gelding should not only be a pleasure to ride, but a winner as well.

Horse #3: There's nothing in the look of the Spanish Barb or even of the Andalusian horse — ancestors of the original "mustangs" of the Great Plains — that would lead an observer to expect the draftiness displayed by this filly purchased from the Bureau of Land Management. Her build is the product of an unfortunate chapter in American history: when native Americans were first confined to reservations, the U.S. government wanted to change them from nomads to farmers. The officials did this by paying bounty hunters to shoot Indian ponies (they got $3 for a pair of ears), and by requiring the Indians to breed draft stallions supplied by the government to their pony and feral mares. For this reason, the Cayuse or Indian pony is now nearly extinct in the United States, and our mustangs are largely crossbreds — nothing like the fleet, compact and agile animals of the nineteenth century.

The owner of this two-year-old assures me that the filly is 14.3 hands, 1,015 pounds and still growing. Although she probably won't top out any taller than 15.1 hands, she'll most likely be quite heavy, perhaps 1,300 pounds as an adult.

If the filly had an excellent set of forelegs, I would recommend her for light draft, utility and trail work. Unfortunately, she also possesses calf knees, which will certainly tend to make her less durable.

Horse #4: This gelding's bucked knees are not an inheritable defect as are the calf knees of Horse #3 and the overstraight front legs of Horse #2. There is such a thing as congenital bucked knees (also called "over at the knee"), but in this individual the bent stance is acquired, either through contracture of the tissues lying on the back of the knee and cannon bones, through strain of the check ligaments during his racing career or a combination of both.

Whether it is acquired or congenital, a buck-kneed stance is an unstable one. Such horses can be ridden, although ultimately I think they are unsafe. In the buck-kneed horse, the axis of the forward-tipped forearm bone (the dashed line in Figure 38) moves the point at which the horse's weight is transferred to the ground abnormally far forward. This is the opposite of the calf-kneed horse, whose weight is borne abnormally far back.

THE FOREQUARTER: LAB EXERCISE 7

The Links Of The Forelimb

How this chain of bones determines the scope and stability of the horse's movements

Now it's time to expand our horizons a bit by examining the angles and proportions of *all* the forelimb's bony elements.

To assess proportionality in the chain of bones forming the horse's forelimb, you can check three key points:

✔ **the point of the shoulder**. How high is this prominence located? Find this point on a horse and use it to mentally construct the shoulder angle as shown in Figure 33. Is this angle open at least 90 degrees? Generally, the higher the point of the shoulder and the wider open the angle formed by the shoulder blade and the upper arm, the greater the scope and freedom of the horse's forelimb movements.

✔ **the knee**. Pretend that the horse's knee is a little elevator that can slide up and down and stop anywhere between the elbow and the fetlock joint. This helps to illustrate that the proportionality of the forearm and cannon are reciprocal: the higher the knee, the shorter the forearm and the longer the cannon. In general, the lower the knee (and thus, the shorter the cannon bone), the stronger and more structurally stable the horse's forelimb.

✔ **the fetlock joint**. With your eye, measure the length from the fetlock joint to the coronary band on a horse's leg. Now mentally compare this length with that of the cannon bone. The pastern segment is too long if it exceeds three-quarters of the length of the cannon and too short if its length is less than half that of the cannon.

With these considerations in mind, let's analyze each of the following four examples.

Analysis

Horse #1: A fine individual with few flaws worth mentioning, this gelding's pelvis (croup) could be a smidgen longer and his withers could be better defined and carry back a bit farther. Everything else is on the positive side. His back, which is no longer than necessary, is particularly pleasing. The coupling is good. The lump that appears in the profile of the topline over the point of the hip is not a pathology but the bulging gluteus medius muscle. Development of this muscle indicates that the horse possesses vigorous, well-suspended gaits and jumping ability. His muscular stifles and gaskins indicate strong, problem-free folding of all three hind-leg joints. His large, well-structured hocks are clean, revealing that the energetic use of his "drive train" isn't harming its structural components at all.

Correct use of the horse's hindquarters has had its usual effect on the muscular development of the neck and back, too. The shoulder is structurally upright and the neck is thick at the root; if this horse had been ridden badly, the lower portion of his neck would be even thicker. There would also be a dip in the topline just in front of the withers and the neck would not look so arched. Good riding and good movement have produced the best possible habitual posture in this gelding.

With his upright shoulder, the angle formed between the gelding's shoulder blade and upper arm at the point of the shoulder is just 90 degrees. The arm length is slightly more than half the length of the shoulder blade. This is not the construction of an Olympic-caliber open jumper, but one which nevertheless predisposes the gelding to pretty, safe performances over medium-sized obstacles.

The gelding's single best feature is his front legs below the breast: his excellent knees, which are well-structured and placed low, lengthen the forearm and shorten the cannon. The pasterns, too, show ideal length and slope. The hooves are the right size and

(1)

(2)

(3)

(4)

(1) **7-year-old Arabian-cross gelding**
(2) **Aged Appaloosa gelding**
(3) **Aged American Saddlebred mare**
(4) **13-year-old grade gelding**

correctly trimmed.

Horse #2: This photograph, taken prior to 1910 on the Kiowa Indian Reservation in Kansas, shows a real Cayuse or Indian pony — actually a lightweight, agile horse standing not more than 15 hands high.

The young warrior had good reason to be proud of his mount: first for his color, which is a combination of "wolf's head" (dark red roan) and "corn" and "zebra" marks. Secondly, note the size and power inherent in the horse's pelvis and quarters as well as how low the stifle joints and hocks are. The horse is undeniably plain about the neck, shoulder and arm; compare the acute angle (less than 90 degrees) at the point of the shoulder to the wide-open angle of Horse #3.

However, such a set of legs is hardly to be found today. This gelding's large knees are ideally "sprung" (slightly bucked). And look at the size of them and of his hocks! As a foal, this Cayuse must have looked like a knob-kneed puppy. His hooves also approach perfection and, having developed on the hard, limy soil of the prairie, they were surely as tough as flint yet as resilient as a hard rubber hockey puck.

From a historical standpoint, the beautiful, individually meaningful saddle appointments and the rider's costume also bear mentioning, as do the wonderful "double S" sweet-iron cavalry bit and the three-quarter-rigged "Mother Hubbard" saddle.

Finally, let us humbly take note of the young warrior's superior position in the saddle. He is totally natural and relaxed, yet his seat would be the envy of many a prize-winning dressage competitor.

Horse #3: This Saddlebred mare has beautiful forequarters *and* hindquarters. Her long shoulder, wide-open shoulder angles, long neck and low, well-set knees are marred only by her slightly long pasterns. The length of her back is compensated by the great length of pelvis, which is fortuitously highlighted by the sun in the photograph. The depth and power of the mare's thighs and gaskins are complemented by her ideally angulated hocks.

Horse #4: Once again, there is a range of acceptable knee angulations. Horse #2 illustrates as much "buck" as I would like to see, while Horse #3 shows as "straight" a foreleg as is called for. This fellow is unfortunately past "overstraight" and into the weak and potentially damaging calf-kneed construction, in which the carpus is angled behind the ideal straight line of front-leg structure when viewed from the side.

The gelding's shoulder and arm construction are good. The point of the shoulder is high and the angle there is 90 degrees. The arm is nearly three-quarters the length of the shoulder. For these reasons, I expect that he has the ability to deliver a decent performance over a course of hunter-sized fences. However, because of his calf knees and very short pasterns, I would be reluctant to jump him.

The Gift Of Lightness

How an uncooperative riding horse was transformed into a graceful, athletic mount

I would like to share a tale of hope and encouragement to all those whose ambition it is not just to keep, but to improve the horses they own and enjoy.

This is the story of my own mare, Sadie, a 21-year-old Arabian-Quarter Horse cross. Sadie spent the second and third years of her life working as a bareback bronc in a third-rate rodeo somewhere in the Great Plains — and she has a matched set of rowel scars on her shoulders to prove it. After that, she spent time with a heavy-handed amateur barrel racer. Fearful of having her sensitive mouth jerked on yet again, one day Sadie reared up and dumped her rider. After that she was sold, and spent the next five years living in a 40-acre pasture where she learned dietary self-sufficiency and became notoriously hard to catch. When her owner got tired of keeping her as a pasture ornament, Sadie was sold to a teen-age girl who stabled her, rode her lightly, hand fed and petted her a lot, and taught her good ground manners and how to stand up for halter class.

I bought Sadie for 60 cents a pound in 1982, when she was 14 years old. That was really more than she was worth, because the very first time I got on her, she reared — the most dangerous behavior a riding horse can exhibit. I responded by lambasting her with a whip behind my leg — and that was the last time she ever reared under saddle.

One success was behind us, but our difficulties were far from over. I knew that Sadie had taken to rearing because, as dressage theory puts it, she had "lost her impulsion" — the natural desire to go forward. I decided that a program of road riding was a practical solution, but it took an investment of time and patience to see the two of us through what came next.

Our first 20 rides were miserable, because Sadie was very barn sour. I had to use spurs or a whip to get her to trot away from the stable. When we turned back, she'd try to dash toward home. I cured her of that habit by making her circle every single time she tried to go faster than I wanted her to. We made hundreds of circles, and if I rode out for an hour, the return trip would take three. She gave up this anxious behavior after the first month, however, and eventually we went on to place in several competitive trail rides. By this time, Sadie was 17 years old and galloping 16-mile loops as part of her conditioning program.

Forward riding across country had restored her impulsion. But because of her history of rough handling in a curb bit, Sadie was still "afraid of her mouth" and unwilling to accept any kind of steady bit contact. When we moved to the East Coast in 1984, I sought expert help in solving this problem, and received it from several professionals who were willing to work with a horse who, rather than being a dressage competitor, was in need of dressage as physical therapy. Regular longeing in side reins, a temporary switch to a flexible rubber bit, work over cavalletti and exercises to increase her lateral flexibility, as well as improvements in my own riding skills, have been major factors in my mare's continual progress.

At long last, Sadie is able and willing to go softly onto the bit, to carry me comfortably and athletically at a sitting trot, to depart on either canter lead with equal ease, and to jump logs and handle up- and downhill terrain while remaining supple and balanced. The greatest wonder of all is that she has achieved self-carriage; that is, she habitually carries at least half of our combined weight with her hind legs.

Figure 39. Good riding and dressage used as physical therapy have improved Sadie's conformation over the seven years I've owned her. A, Sadie's forelegs in 1986. The plumb line shows that she stood base narrow, with tight elbows and toes that pointed out. Sadie's forelegs in 1988, age 20. Notice how much looser her elbows are and how much squarer her breast box is. C, Sadie in 1983 while we wait our turn for a dressage test. The lower triangle of her neck is hollow, and the rhomboideus and brachiocephalicus muscles are dominant. The complexus muscle is not evident. Her quarters look flat and angular; her groin is high and she shows a "waist." D, Sadie in 1985; the lower triangle of her neck is fuller, and the upper part of the complexus muscle can be seen. The brachiocephalicus is smaller, but the rhomboideus is now much too big. Her quarters are fuller and her groin has dropped; she shows less waist between ribs and hips. E, Sadie in 1989, age 21. The whole posture of her neck has changed; because her scalenus muscle (not visible from the outside) is now strong, the root of her neck is supported internally and thus her neck appears to come off her withers and shoulders much higher than in the "old days" when she was a mere teenager. Her quarters, especially the gluteal area (on top), and the "pants muscle" (on the side of the thigh) are full. Her waist has entirely disappeared. Other pictures of Sadie are shown in Figure 14. At the present time, we're working to improve her lateral work (traverse), and hoping to see piaffe next year.

As a result of her relaxed, rounded and stretched topline, and of her active use of her belly and hind-limb muscles, Sadie has achieved a degree of lightness. This means that there is less weight pressing down onto her forelimbs with each stride. This, in turn, relieves her breast and forearm muscles of the need to stiffen in order to stabilize her forelegs.

Our years of working together have made a noticeable difference in Sadie's conformation, and thus, in her usefulness as a riding horse (Fig. 14). What greater gift can a horse and rider give to one another?

A

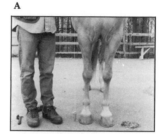

B

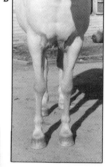

C

D

E

Appendix A

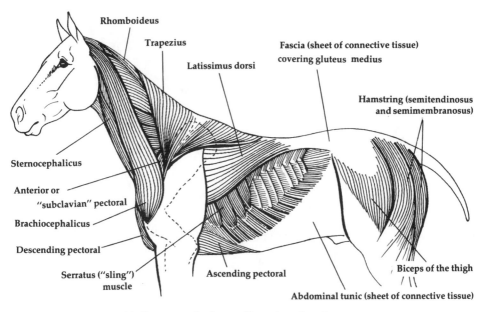

Rhomboideus

Trapezius

Latissimus dorsi

Fascia (sheet of connective tissue) covering gluteus medius

Hamstring (semitendinosus and semimembranosus)

Sternocephalicus

Anterior or "subclavian" pectoral

Brachiocephalicus

Descending pectoral

Serratus ("sling") muscle

Ascending pectoral

Biceps of the thigh

Abdominal tunic (sheet of connective tissue)

Shallow muscular layer of horse's neck and torso

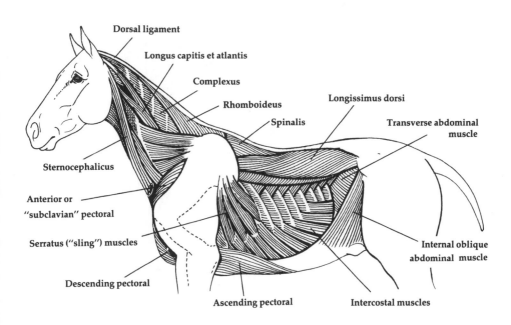

Dorsal ligament

Longus capitis et atlantis

Complexus

Rhomboideus

Spinalis

Longissimus dorsi

Transverse abdominal muscle

Sternocephalicus

Anterior or "subclavian" pectoral

Serratus ("sling") muscles

Descending pectoral

Ascending pectoral

Intercostal muscles

Internal oblique abdominal muscle

Deep layer of torso and neck muscles. For deepest layer of neck muscles, see Fig. 22.

Appendix B

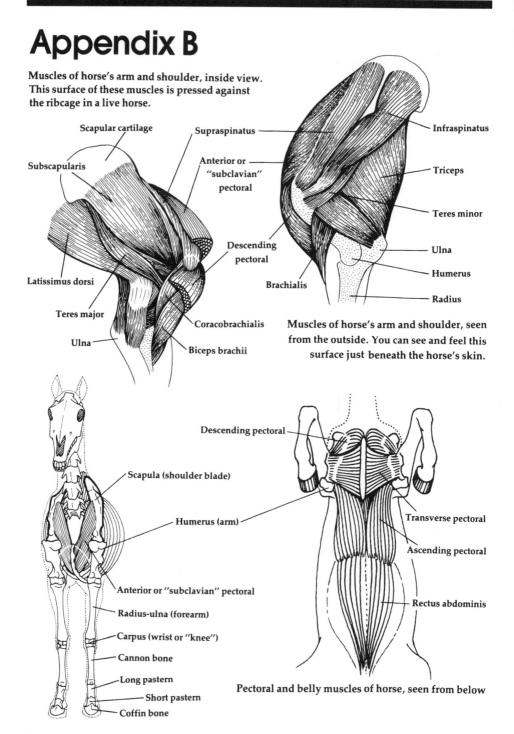

Muscles of horse's arm and shoulder, inside view. This surface of these muscles is pressed against the ribcage in a live horse.

Scapular cartilage
Subscapularis
Supraspinatus
Anterior or "subclavian" pectoral
Infraspinatus
Triceps
Teres minor
Ulna
Humerus
Radius
Descending pectoral
Latissimus dorsi
Teres major
Ulna
Coracobrachialis
Biceps brachii
Brachialis

Muscles of horse's arm and shoulder, seen from the outside. You can see and feel this surface just beneath the horse's skin.

Scapula (shoulder blade)
Humerus (arm)
Anterior or "subclavian" pectoral
Radius-ulna (forearm)
Carpus (wrist or "knee")
Cannon bone
Long pastern
Short pastern
Coffin bone

Descending pectoral
Transverse pectoral
Ascending pectoral
Rectus abdominis

Pectoral and belly muscles of horse, seen from below

Pectoral muscles as seen from the front. The anterior or "subclavian" pectoral muscle is overlain by the descending and transverse pectoral muscles. The white line shows the upper border of the descending part as it appears in front view.